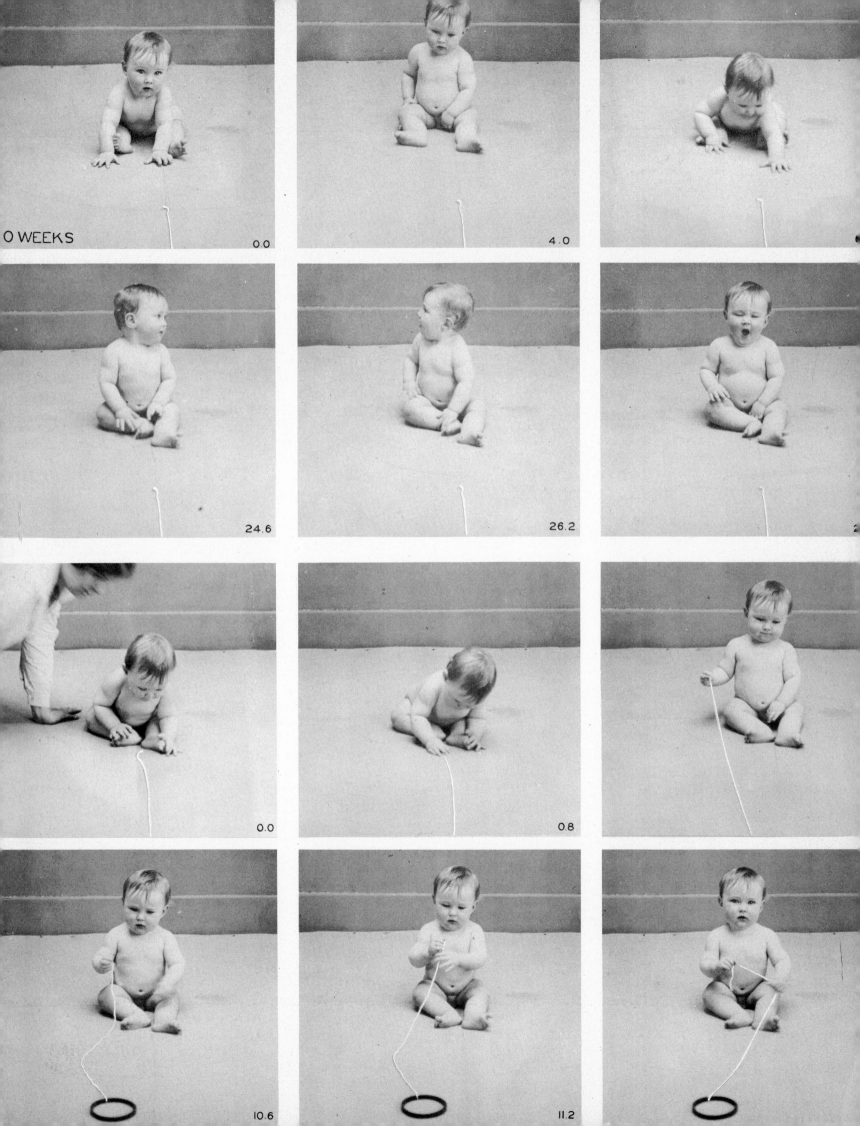

O WEEKS

0.0

4.0

24.6

26.2

0.0

0.8

10.6

11.2

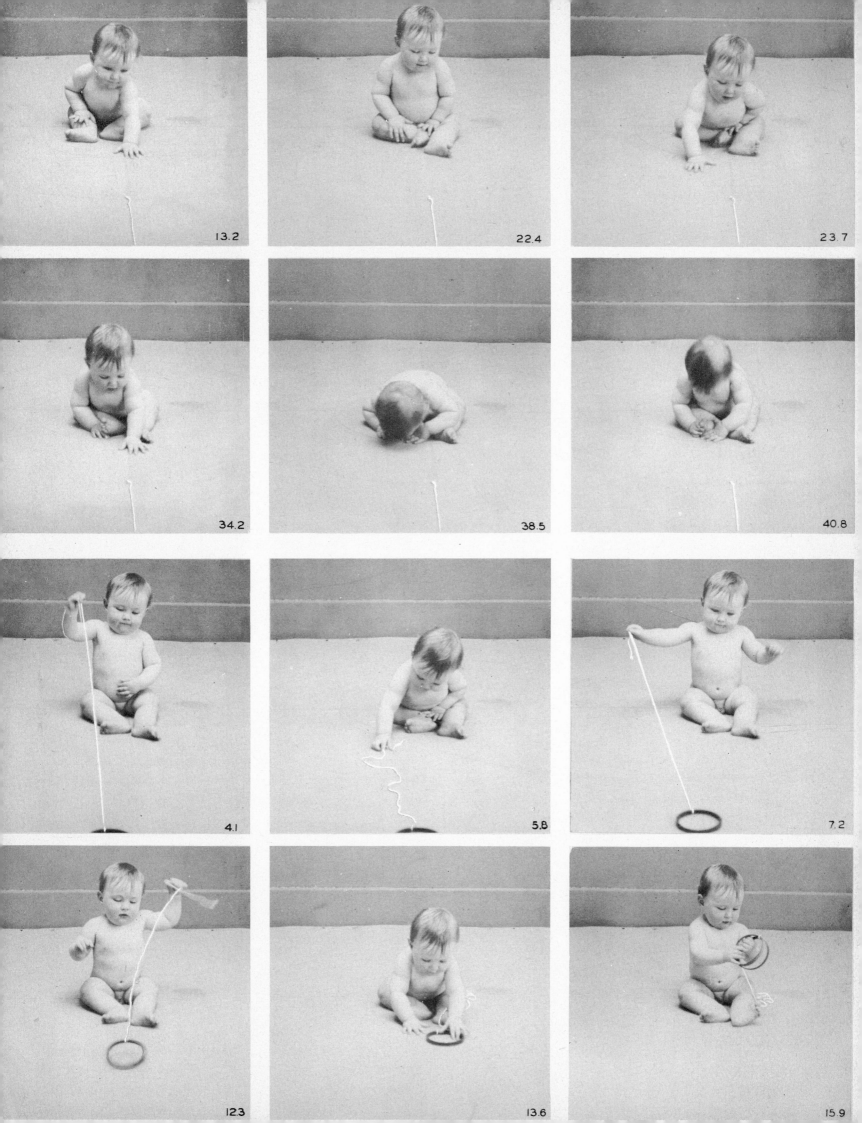

# HOW
# A BABY GROWS
## A Story in Pictures

# BOOKS BY ARNOLD GESELL

THE NORMAL CHILD AND PRIMARY EDUCATION (with B. C. Gesell)

EXCEPTIONAL CHILDREN AND PUBLIC SCHOOL POLICY

HANDICAPPED CHILDREN IN SCHOOL AND COURT

THE PRE-SCHOOL CHILD FROM THE STANDPOINT
OF PUBLIC HYGIENE AND EDUCATION

THE RETARDED CHILD—HOW TO HELP HIM

THE MENTAL GROWTH OF THE PRE-SCHOOL CHILD

INFANCY AND HUMAN GROWTH

GUIDANCE OF MENTAL GROWTH IN INFANT AND CHILD

AN ATLAS OF INFANT BEHAVIOR (two volumes, 3,200 action photographs)

INFANT BEHAVIOR—ITS GENESIS AND GROWTH (with Thompson)

THE FEEDING BEHAVIOR OF INFANTS—A PEDIATRIC APPROACH
TO THE MENTAL HYGIENE OF EARLY LIFE (with Ilg)

THE PSYCHOLOGY OF EARLY GROWTH (with Thompson)

BIOGRAPHIES OF CHILD DEVELOPMENT

THE FIRST FIVE YEARS OF LIFE:—A GUIDE TO THE STUDY
OF THE PRE-SCHOOL CHILD

WOLF CHILD AND HUMAN CHILD

TWINS T AND C FROM INFANCY TO ADOLESCENCE (with Thompson)

DEVELOPMENTAL DIAGNOSIS: CLINICAL METHODS
AND PRACTICAL APPLICATIONS (with Amatruda)

INFANT AND CHILD IN THE CULTURE OF TODAY (with Ilg)

THE EMBRYOLOGY OF BEHAVIOR

A GUIDE TO THE STUDY OF THE YALE FILMS OF CHILD DEVELOPMENT

These films depict the mental growth and the behavior characteristics of the first five years of life. *The films are distributed by* Encyclopedia Britannica Films, Inc., 1841 Broadway, New York City.

### INFANT AND CHILD IN THE CULTURE OF TODAY (with Ilg)

This book deals, age by age, with the guidance of child development in home and nursery school. It gives a fuller account of methods of child care and of child management (400 pages). *Published by* Harper & Brothers, 49 East 33rd Street, New York City.

# HOW A BABY GROWS

## A Story in Pictures

*By*

### ARNOLD GESELL, M.D.

DIRECTOR OF THE CLINIC OF CHILD DEVELOPMENT
YALE UNIVERSITY

OVER 800 PHOTOGRAPHS
ARRANGED AND INTERPRETED

*With the assistance of*

KATHERINE GESELL WALDEN, A.B.

HARPER & BROTHERS · PUBLISHERS

NEW YORK AND LONDON

69295

To
S U S A N
and
to
P E T E R
and
to
A N N E
and
to
P A T R I C I A

# Table of Contents

PART TWO

# THE BABY IN THE HOME

*His Personality Takes Shape in a Social World*

# A brief word to

# the reader of these pictures

THE pictures tell their own story. In them the baby comes to life. We see him (and her!) exploring the world with eyes, mouth, hands, feet; staring, inspecting, wondering; smiling, laughing, crying; sitting, standing, rolling, creeping, climbing, walking, romping; falling asleep and waking again to renew inquisitive touching, grasping, poking, listening, prying, experimenting.

We see the baby eating, drinking, bathing, playing; building with blocks, drawing with crayons, painting with brush; communicating, gesticulating, dramatizing,—ceaselessly manipulating *THE WORLD OF THINGS;* also penetrating deeper and deeper into *THE WORLD OF PERSONS.*

He is a very busy person in these pages. But the purpose of our book is not simply to portray his endless activities. Behind and within these activities there is a growing mind, a developing personality. We have arranged the pictures with care to indicate the hidden forces of growth which shape the baby's behavior day by day, month by month. We invite the reader to read the pictures in such a way that they will tell again this story of growth.

[ 1 ]

# ONE YEAR OF MENTAL GROWTH:
## A panoramic view

NOTHING is so obvious as a baby. And yet he eludes us. He grows so rapidly that he almost escapes our understanding.

We can follow his physical growth by watching his gains in ounces and inches. But we would also like to follow the growth of his mind. Can we do that?

We can, if we read the pictures and look for the evidences of growth there revealed. The camera has caught the outward signs of the growing mind. As the baby grows his behavior changes in shape. It takes on new forms, new patterns. At 16 weeks he stares at a block on the table. At 24 weeks he reaches for the block on sight. (A more advanced behavior pattern.) This is how the mind of a baby grows.

The pictures on the opposite page sum up the transformations in behavior pattern which take place in the first year of life. Later pages tell a fuller story. All the pictures are designed to show average or near average trends of development.

It must be remembered, however, that in actual life no one baby will show all these average trends. Babies are individuals. They have distinctive personalities. *Every baby has his own way of growing up. No baby follows exactly an average time table.* So the reader is advised not to try to measure a baby's intelligence simply by means of the pictures.

After all, intelligence is only one phase of the baby's mind. Our first task is to understand the way in which the whole baby grows.

The first part of our book will tell how the baby gains control of his body and how he begins the conquest of his physical environment.

PART TWO will tell more of his emotional life and how he makes his adjustments to the social world of the home.

But he doesn't grow in two parts. He grows as a unit, and from the moment of birth he is an individual personality.

[ 2 ]

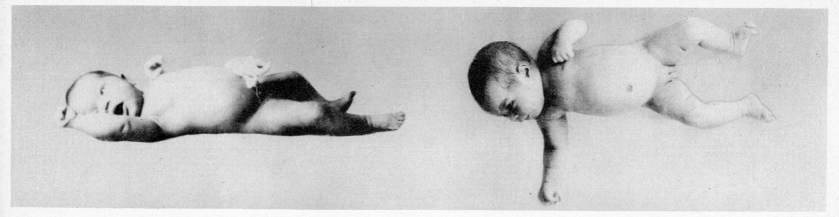

1 WEEK: Holds head rotated to the side                    6 WEEKS: Stares at wall

 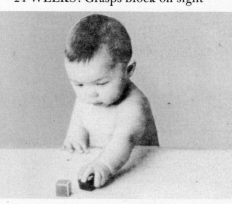

*2 month* 8 WEEKS: Holds ring without inspecting it    *3 month* 12 WEEKS: Follows moving object with eyes

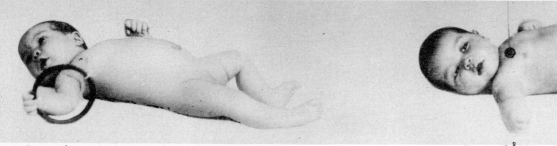

*4 mos* 16 WEEKS: Looks fixedly at block on table    *5 month* 20 WEEKS: Contacts spoon    *6 month* 24 WEEKS: Grasps block on sight

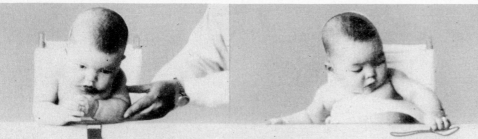 

*7 month* 28 WEEKS: Bangs block    *8 month* 32 WEEKS: Rakes pellet    36 WEEKS: Goes after second block

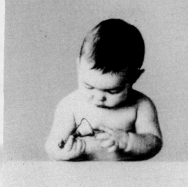   

*10 months* 40 WEEKS: Pokes bell    *11 mos* 44 WEEKS: Picks pellet between fore-finger and thumb    *1 year* 48 WEEKS: Recovers block from under cup    52 WEEKS: Brings crayon to paper

# PART ONE

# THE
# BABY GROWS UP

He gains control of his body and exploits
the physical world

# INFANT EYES: *Vision is a pathfinder.*

VISION leads in the early growth of the mind. The baby uses his eyes before he uses his hands. He can see before he can reach. He is born with twelve tiny muscles which move his eyes left and right, up and down. Even before he was born the muscles began to operate, as a preparation for the later business of looking and seeing.

During the first twelve weeks after birth the eyes are brought under increasing control. It takes time for this control to mature. It is not surprising that even the normal baby sometimes looks cross-eyed. The eyes cross and get out of line when balanced control has not yet been gained. At 24 weeks he moves his eyes alertly; eyes and hands come into joint action. As he grows older the teamwork between eyes and hands improves. This is one reason why he looks so intently at whatever he does with his busy fingers. The eyes are pathfinders for the hands.

**A Four-Weeks-Old Baby Stares Vacantly. The Twelve Tiny Muscles Which Move His Eye Balls Mature Slowly.**

He can feel the feather on his brow and foot but cannot look at it. He will not look at the rattle (picture No. 2) until about 20 weeks of age.

**At Six Weeks the Eye Muscles Are Beginning to Co-ordinate Efficiently. Note How This Baby's Eyes Follow the Ring.**

 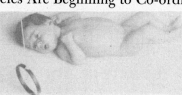  

As the dangling ring moves past him, this six-weeks-old baby's eyes follow it for only a short distance.
At 20 weeks he will turn both head and eyes in pursuit of a moving object.

### At 12 Weeks—

  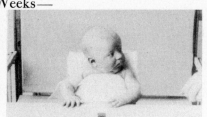 

The eyes shift from table . . .          . . . to his own hand . . .          . . . to the examiner's hand . . .          . . . to the cube.

### At 24 Weeks—

 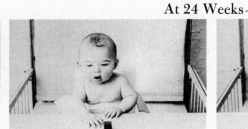  

The eyes are alert.          They fix on one cube . . .          They glance at a second cube . . .          But return to the first cube.

### This Baby's Eyes Express the Growth of Individuality

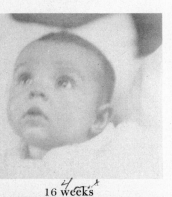 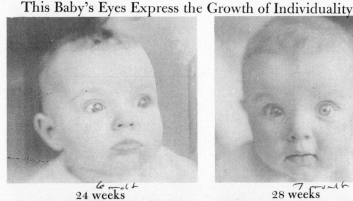  

16 weeks          24 weeks          28 weeks          32 weeks

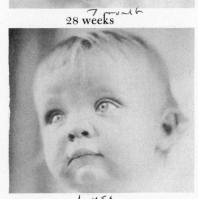  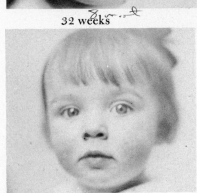

36 weeks          44 weeks          48 weeks          80 weeks

The clear eyes of the infant mirror his fresh outlook on the world. Note that as this baby grows the eyes take on character and individuality. In conjunction with the muscles of face and mouth, the eyes express the baby's moods and emotions.
Very early, too, the baby looks at the human face and learns to read the emotions of others.

# INFANT HANDS: *They learn to co-operate with the eyes.*

EYES lead and hands follow in the story of growth. First the two eyes must coordinate with each other and then the eyes must coordinate with the hands. When the eyes and hands coordinate in good teamwork the baby's conquest of the physical world gets well under way.

His fingers are levers and feelers combined. He pries with his fingers and his eyes. There are thousands of sensitive nerve endings in his finger joints and finger tips. These nerve endings are the sentinels of the sensitive skin. Thousands of nerve fibers connect the hand with the brain. Mind and brain grow together. The pictures at the right show that this growth begins in the prenatal period. The young baby uses his hand like a paw, but at the end of the first year he brings thumb and forefinger together in neat and skillful opposition.

The Prenatal Hand: These drawings show, step by step, how it takes shape, eventually becomes this—The Hand at Birth

Early in the prenatal period the hand takes shape; nerve fibers grow into the many muscles of shoulders, arms, fingers.
Step by step these muscles come under brain control. Early grasping is pawlike; later grasping deft and delicate.

## From Birth to One Year the Human Hand Grows in Dexterity

 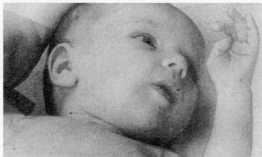 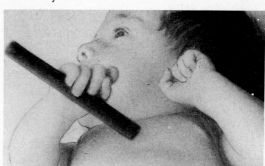

The newborn hand is a mere cup.　　　At 4 weeks the thumb is idle and useless.　　　At 6 weeks the outside fingers are strongest.

 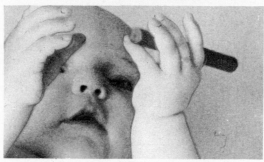 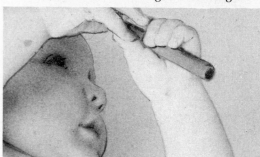

At 20 weeks the grasp is a squeeze.　　　At 24 weeks the fingers still get tangled with the object.　　　At 28 weeks one hand takes the object from the other hand.

 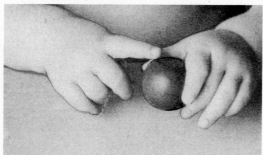 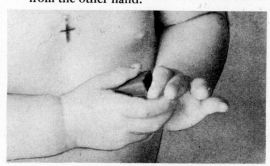

At 32 weeks the inside fingers become most important.　　　At 44 weeks forefinger and thumb are specialized.　　　At 52 weeks thumb opposes forefinger with almost adult skill.

## Similar Twins — Similar Anatomy — Similar Maturity — Similar Patterns of Pellet Prehension

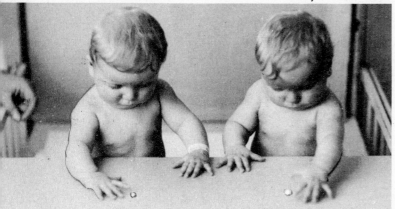 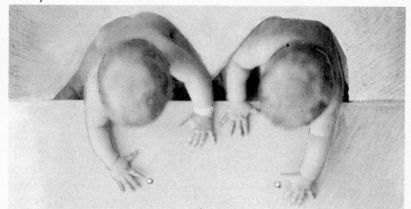

Mind and body grow as one. The inborn identity of these twins makes their behavior patterns as well as their body patterns alike.
(The picture at the right is an overhead shot taken simultaneously with the picture at the left.)

# INFANT FEET: *At first superfluous. At last the foundation of erect posture.*

Eyes Discover the Feet. Hands Manipulate Them. Feet as Hands! — And Hands as Feet

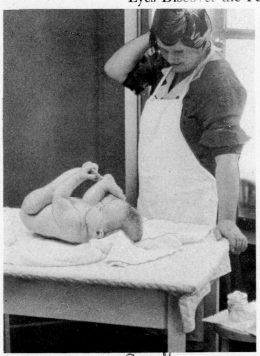

At 20 weeks

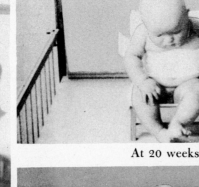

At 28 weeks

At 40 weeks

They walk: At 60 months, and at 60 weeks

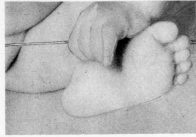

Reaches with foot and hand.

Holds bottle with feet.

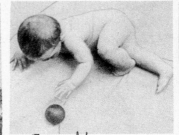

At 36 weeks: Turns body, using hands for footwork... and then...

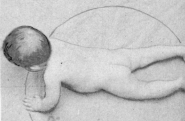

Pulls self toward ball with hands.

Eyes early, feet late. The feet are the last suburbs to be knit into the growing nervous system. They lie farthest from the head and not until the connecting nerve fibers and nerve centers are ripe do the feet become obedient to the brain. And so upright posture is finally achieved.

There are seven main stages in the growth of human posture and locomotion: (1) recliner, (2) roller, (3) sitter, (4) creeper, (5) cruiser, (6) toddler, (7) runabout. Feet are relatively unimportant for the first four stages, but indispensable for the rest. Each stage of locomotion widens the radius of the child's experience and increases his sense of power.

### This 48-Weeks-Old Baby Takes a Short and Somewhat Unsteady Walk

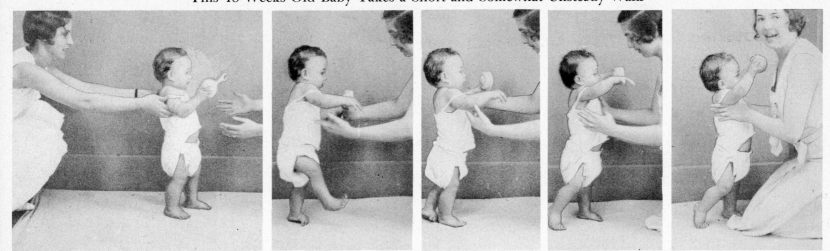

### But Now See the Same Baby. At 52 Weeks He Walks Across the Room

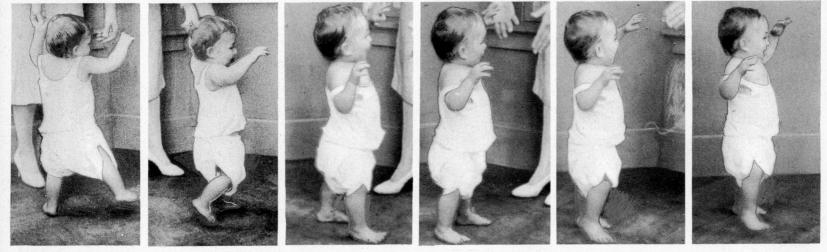

### Bipedal Locomotion at 68 Weeks—At This Age Babies Walk and Squat on a Wide Base

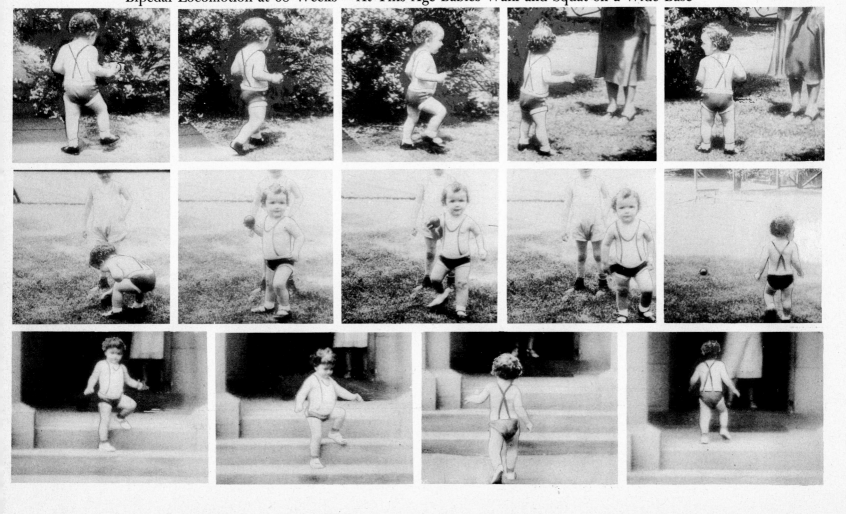

# CREEPING: *Growth advances stage by stage.*

IT takes a long time before a baby can stand alone on his two feet. For most of the first year he goes on fours instead of on twos. He uses hands and knees before he travels by foot, because it is easier to balance a horizontal trunk than a vertical one. At first he lies on chest and stomach. Later he rests his entire weight on palms and soles. Not till the end of the first year does he become a "biped." The photographs on the opposite page picture five stages of growth which precede the assumption of the erect posture. There are many other stages interesting to observe. They are temporary, but they all prepare for the climax of standing and walking alone.

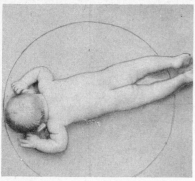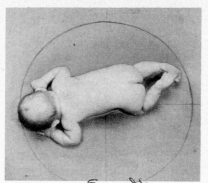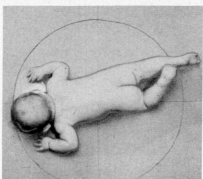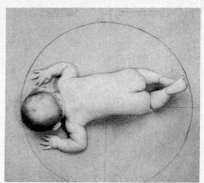

ANCHORED TO THE SPOT: At 20 weeks he may draw up his knees but he cannot make headway.

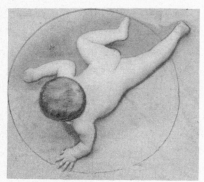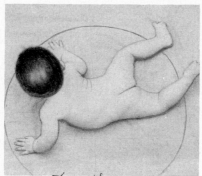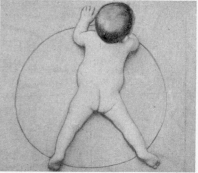

PIVOTS IN A CIRCLE: At about 32 weeks arms are more skillful than legs. By working his arms he pivots around.

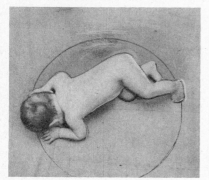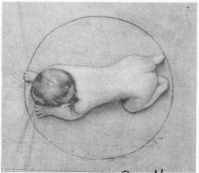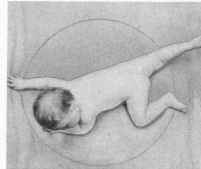

PROGRESSES—BACKWARD! At 36 weeks his legs still lag; consequently he goes backward.

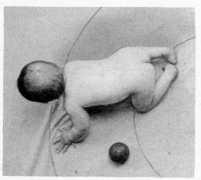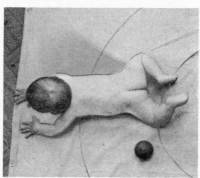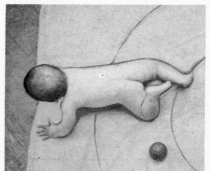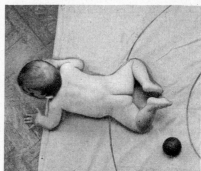

HALF CRAWLS, HALF CREEPS: Later he advances by falling forward from creep position.

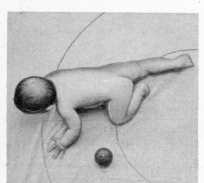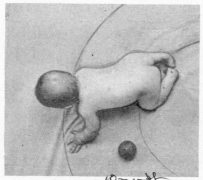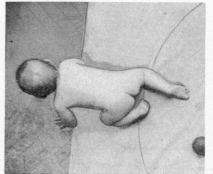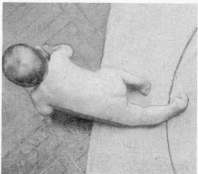

CREEPS FORWARD: At about 40 weeks he alternates hands and knees in true creeping fashion.

# BABIES ARE NOT ALIKE: *Every baby has an individual pattern of growth.*

BABIES pass through similar stages of growth, but not on the same time table. Here are five healthy babies all of whom have developed into normal, intelligent school children. But at 40 weeks of age one of these babies was backward in locomotion; one was advanced. The other three were near average. Each child had his own growth schedule even though the order of stages was much alike for all five.

At 40 weeks of age Baby *One* lifts arms and kicks legs, but makes no progress. Baby *Two* crawls on his stomach, chiefly by dragging himself forward with his arms. Baby *Three* gets into a creep position, holds it a moment and falls forward, a combination of creep and crawl. Baby *Four* plants one hand, digs in his opposite knee and creeps. Baby *Five* travels plantigrade, on hands and soles,—four-footed fashion, like a quadruped.

But all of these babies became true bipeds in due time. This is a good reminder that babies are individuals. Every baby inherits certain factors which determine the timing and the style of his growth.

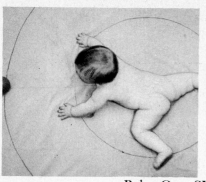 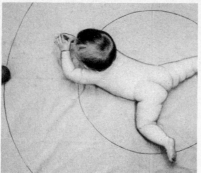  

Baby One **SWIMS** Without Headway: He lifts arms and kicks legs but makes no progress.

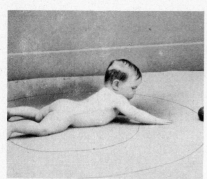  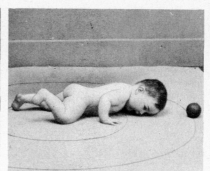 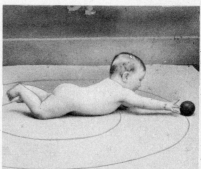

Baby Two **CRAWLS** by Arm Drag: He crawls on stomach, propelling self with arms.

Baby Three **CREEP-CRAWLS**: He gets into creep position, holds it a moment, then falls forward
—a combination of CREEP and CRAWL.

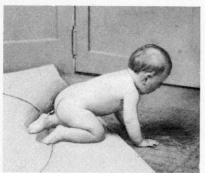 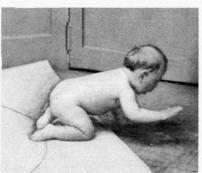 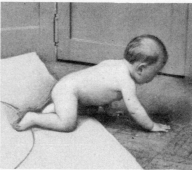 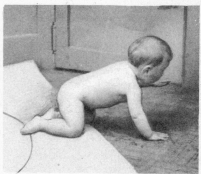

Baby Four **CREEPS**: He plants one hand, digs in opposite knee, and creeps by alternating lift and push.

Baby Five **GOES-ON-ALL-FOURS**: Like a bear, he plants foot as well as hand, in true quadruped manner.

# NATURAL EXERCISE: *Activity promotes healthy growth.*

GROWING creatures are active. The baby knows best what movements are good for him. Many movements he cannot make because his nervous system is not ripe enough. Look at the 8 weeks old baby on the opposite page. His motions are simple, but they are natural and beneficial. As he grows older his nerve cells ripen and send new branches to his growing muscles. He begins to do new things.

He gets a thrill from using his large muscles unrestrained. Give him the chance. Protect his safety; then let him roll, pivot and kick. A hard bed, a roomy table or tub, and a warm floor are his athletic fields. Let him try out his athletic abilities. Nature knows what he is ready for. It is not wise to teach him fancy acrobatics. Let him invent his self-exercises. Through natural exercises he discovers and organizes his own powers.

## Activity Is a Condition of Healthy Growth. Even the Very Young Baby Brandishes His Arms and Kicks His Legs

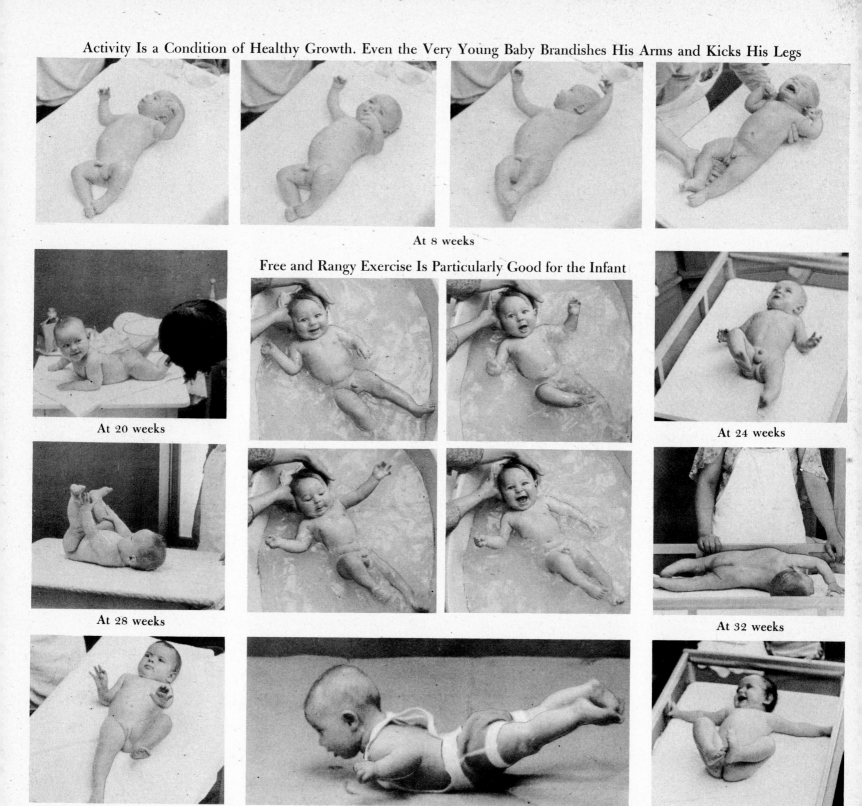

At 8 weeks

### Free and Rangy Exercise Is Particularly Good for the Infant

At 20 weeks

At 24 weeks

At 28 weeks

At 32 weeks

At 36 weeks

A 16-weeks-old baby tries "swimming" on the floor.

At 44 weeks

## The Baby from Month to Month Creates His Own Exercises. At 44 Weeks This Baby Takes a Rich Variety

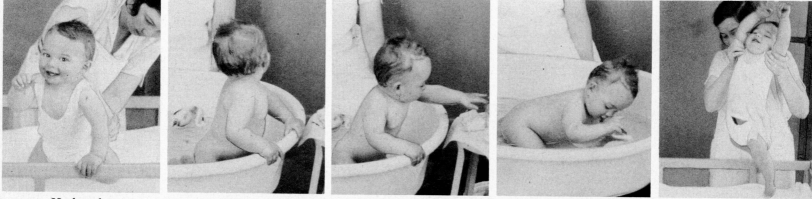

He kneels.  He twists.  He reaches.  He splashes.  He stretches.

# SLEEP: *A prime essential for healthful growth.*

THE baby grows while he sleeps. During sleep nature gets in her chemical handiwork and builds his food and his experiences into growing tissues. So each morning he wakes not only rested but more mature.

As you will note by the pictures, the baby does not always wait for a conventional time and place to sleep. His impromptu naps are as beneficial to him as his food. Nature knows his needs.

Daytime naps are as important as night-time sleep. Outdoor air is usually best. The baby must be snug and warm. He should not be bound too tightly; but take good care not to have his hood and his blankets so loose that he might smother. Pillows and bags which are too tightly anchored also are a hazard.

To prevent accidental smothering be especially careful about sleeping arrangements in the first six months. Do not use any garment or sleeping bag that locks or binds around the neck. Do not use too many blankets (dress the Baby warmly instead in cold weather). Tuck the blankets under a firm mattress and clip them with a big clip, so they will not press down too tightly. The Baby should have leeway to move and to breathe!

It is entirely normal for a baby to stir while asleep. Babies show their individuality in the way they wake as well as in the way they sleep. Yawning has its uses. It drives more blood to the drowsy brain. Stretching also hastens the flow of blood as chest swells and heart beats with new vigor.

## The Camera Shows a 12-Weeks-Old Baby as He Alternately Goes to Sleep and Awakes

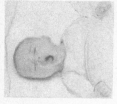    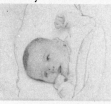  

| Drowsy | Sleepy | Asleep | Awake | Sleepy | Asleep | Waking |

## A 28-Weeks-Old Baby: It Is Natural for a Baby to Change His Posture During Sleep

| Head turns | On side | Stirring | Hand back | Hand out |

## Camera Records a Split Second, as Sleep Comes to a 16-Weeks-Old Baby

## The Baby Doesn't Wait for a Conventional Time or Place to Sleep

One eye closed · Both eyes closed in sleep

Hungry . . . · and sleepy

Doesn't wake when lifted . . . · Falls sound asleep

## 24 Weeks Old, This Baby Is Content to Nap Even if Left Alone

| Wide awake now | Getting drowsy | Eyes going shut | A yawn | Asleep |

## A 12-Weeks-Old Baby Awakes

 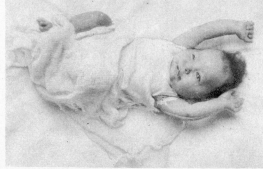 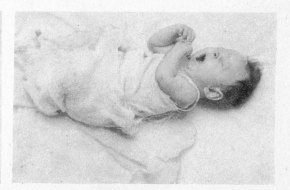

Sleep ends. · He stretches. · He yawns.

# *The Sense of Touch is the Basis of Knowledge.*

INFANTS are by nature investigators and experimenters. They tingle with touch-inquisitiveness. Instinct impels them to handle everything they touch. By constant manipulation and mouthing and inspection the infant learns the form, size, weight, edges, and texture of things.

Instinctive manipulation makes every infant a discoverer. We cannot teach him the nature of things by words. He must learn for himself by exploring with his own eyes, mouth, and hands. Thousands of nerve fibers connect the fingers with the brain. The hands inform and ultimately obey the brain.

**The Baby Is His Own Teacher.** He is born with the urge to find out what the world is like. Looking is not enough. He must also mouth, touch, handle, squeeze, push, pull, and test out The World of Things.

### The Baby Can See Ring, but He Is Not Satisfied Until He Handles It

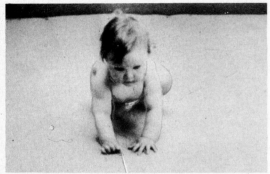  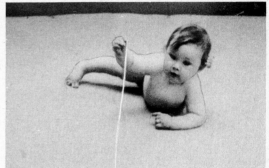

This 48-weeks-old baby sees the ring . . .     But he is not satisfied . . .     Until he pulls it . . .

Near enough . . .     To reach . . .     To feel and to handle.

### Babies Can Learn the Nature of Things only by Constant Exploring and Experimentation

   (img cluster)

Whether sitting or standing, growing babies are under an urge to touch, to manipulate, to investigate.

Lowers     Kneels     Grasps and squeezes doll     Cruises

# PLAY: *The exercise of growing powers.*

PLAY is the infant's work. Play is the exercise of growing powers. In play he instinctively tries out his abilities. He kicks his legs and brandishes his arms; he fingers, handles and bangs; he inspects, he babbles, he imitates. By ceaseless play he gathers experience.

Play is of two kinds: individual and social. Both are essential to mental growth. When the Baby plays by himself he learns independence and self reliance. When he plays with others he learns to please his playmates as well as himself.

The simplest objects like a washrag, a towel, water, clothespins, boxes, string, paper, serve well as playthings. Expensive toys are unnecessary. Too many toys at a time confuse.

## The Beginnings of Hide and Seek!

Even a baby . . .

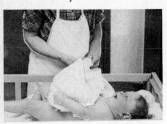

can invent . . .

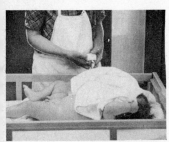

his own games.

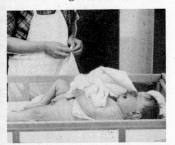

This baby is 28 weeks old.

## The Simplest Objects Serve Well for Playthings

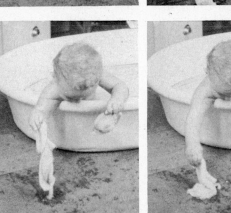

## The Beginnings of Co-operative Play

The three-year-old . . .

boy starts a game . . .

and helps his . . .

baby brother (28 weeks)

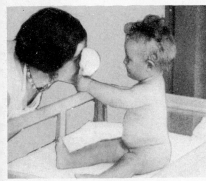
Social approach . . .

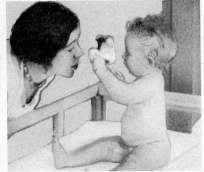
and withdrawal.

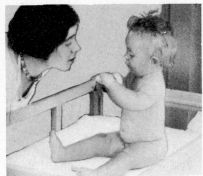
Independent investigation.

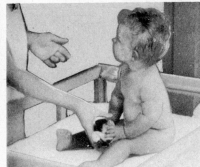
Give and take. (48 weeks old)

The 5-year-old boy has a plan.

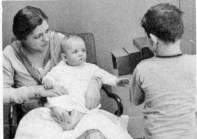
He invents a camera.

The 28-weeks-old baby crows.

A close up.

# THE BATH: *It is an educational experience.*

THE important event of the Baby's Behavior Day is the Bath! It brings welcome release from clothes and gives a healthy freedom for body, legs, arms. It brings cod liver oil and orange or tomato juice. It creates social experiences in which mother and child come to understand each other.

The bath is an educational event charged with psychological as well as hygienic values. Emotions as well as muscles are active. Calm and confident handling helps to make the occasion enjoyable for both mother and child.

There are many different ways to give a bath. But here is a good one: a low stand with a large tub for the baby and a low stool for the mother. With this arrangement the baby has a genuine chance to exercise. Calisthenics are hardly necessary!

The bath ceases to be a chore when it is converted into an educational opportunity.

## Eight Weeks

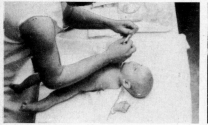   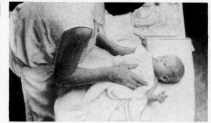

Gentle but sure handling     Vitamins in oil and juice     A mild soap scrub     A tingling towel

## Sixteen Weeks

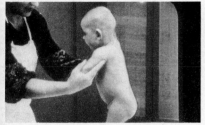   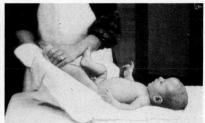

Freedom      Hygiene      Exercise      Relaxation

## Water Sport and Exercise at 24 Weeks!

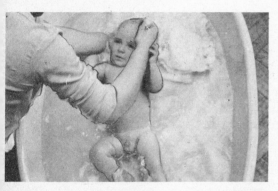  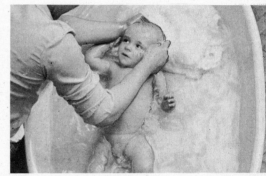

 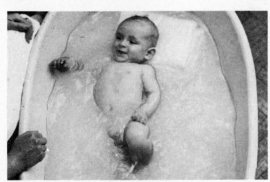 

A large tub, firm on the floor, has many advantages at this age. A folded towel under the head makes free leg strokes possible.

## Twenty-eight Weeks

The fun begins.    He goes for the swan.    He grabs and misses.    But . . .    retrieves.

## Fifty-two Weeks

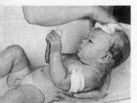 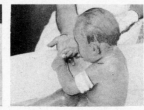 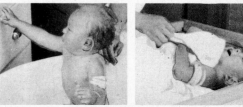

While mother shampoos . . . he holds the soap.    He floats it.    He surrenders it.    He explores.   The vaccination dressing is kept dry.

# SITTING: *A half-way station on the road to standing.*

BABIES sit before they stand. It takes a whole year to attain the full upright posture. Sitting is a halfway stage. At first the infant lies on his back. Then he begins to lift his head forward, but it wobbles and bobs. When he can firmly balance his head, at about 20 weeks, he may be placed in the sitting position for short periods, if he is well propped by pillows.

He cannot sit without support, because the muscles and nerves of his trunk are still immature. He likes to sit, but he fatigues and fusses if he sits too long. Even later, with the support of a chair he may tire quickly. Most children can sit alone at the age of 36 weeks. The average trend is pictured on the opposite page. But remember that babies differ and do not all follow the same time schedule.

# This Is How a Baby Learns to Sit Up, Month by Month. One Year's Progress in Review

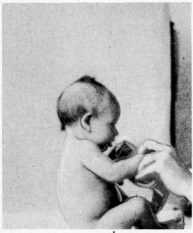

8 weeks
Much too young to sit

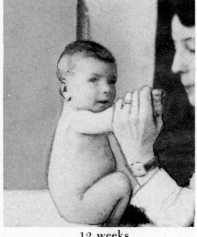

12 weeks
Back is rounded

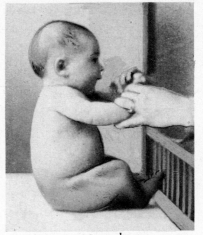

16 weeks
Head is steadier

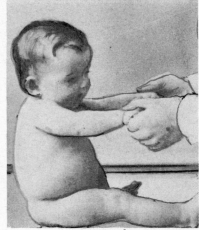

20 weeks
Trunk is firmer

24 weeks
Sits if propped

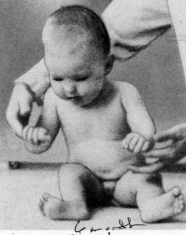

24 weeks
But falls sideward

28 weeks
Sits by leaning on hands

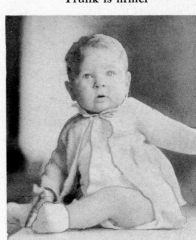

32 weeks
Sits alone a brief moment

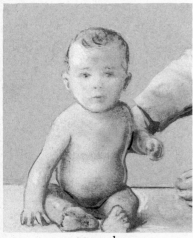

32 weeks
Balances a moment

36 weeks
Sits alone

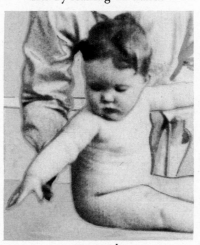

40 weeks
Turns to side

At 52 weeks he has
mastered sitting.

## This Baby, at 48 Weeks, Can Sit Up Well Enough to Study His Own Image in the Mirror

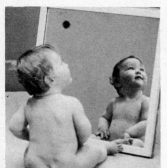

He looks around.

He looks at image.

Another sideward glance.

He leans toward image.

It's still a mystery to him.

# THE BABY STANDS: *and Frees his Hands.*

THE erect posture was one of the greatest achievements of the human race. It is an important event in the development of the child. The ability to stand comes by slow degrees. As early as 24 weeks the Baby likes to be held in the standing position, stepping and bouncing. At about 32 weeks he can support his entire weight, but he cannot balance himself. He clings for support.

Not until the close of the first year or later does he stand altogether alone. He enjoys creeping, but an inner urge drives him to his feet. He pulls himself up. At 40 weeks (or thereabouts) he stands holding fast with his hands. Later he cruises, still holding on. Before 18 months he usually walks alone. This frees his hands for further conquests of the physical world.

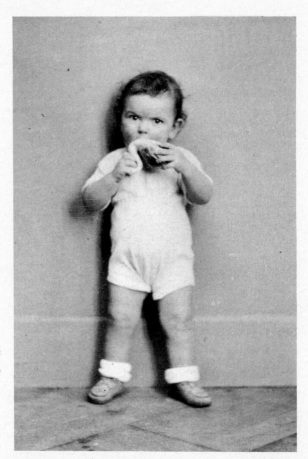

It takes a whole year or more
to achieve the erect posture.

## As Early as 24 Weeks the Baby Likes to Be Held in Standing Position. He Steps and Bounces.

     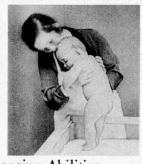

### At 40 Weeks He Likes to Stand, Holding to Crib

### At About 44 Weeks He May Try Balancing Abilities

He lifts one foot and then the other, but stays on the spot. Later he learns to cruise around the crib, using hands to assist feet. Cruising is midway between creeping and walking.

Now and then when all is safe, the baby may try out his balancing abilities. But standing will come from a natural inner urge, when the nerve centers ripen. Do not try to hasten standing. Let nature decide when the time is ripe.

### At About 48 Weeks the Baby Learns to Cruise Around Crib, Using Hands to Assist Feet
#### (Cruising is halfway stage between creeping and walking)

 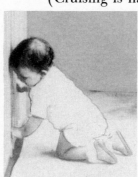     

### Six Progressive Stages in the Ascent from Horizontal to Upright

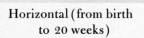

| Horizontal (from birth to 20 weeks) | Sits upright, supported | Sits alone (about 36 weeks) | Stands supported (40 weeks) | Stands alone (52 weeks) | Walks (64 weeks) |

# PART TWO

# THE
# BABY IN THE HOME

His personality takes shape in a social world —
a world of persons

# INFANT AND FAMILY: *The household is the first school.*

SOCIAL training can come only through experience. The Baby learns about persons in the same manner that he learns about things,—by coming into contact with them. From the beginning it is a game of give and take for all ages. The game goes best in a companionable atmosphere where no one expects too much of the other.

Companionship in the home livened by humor is the best first school for training in social behavior. The enrollment in this school includes father, mother, the baby and his brothers and sisters.

The household socializes the baby and the baby socializes the household.

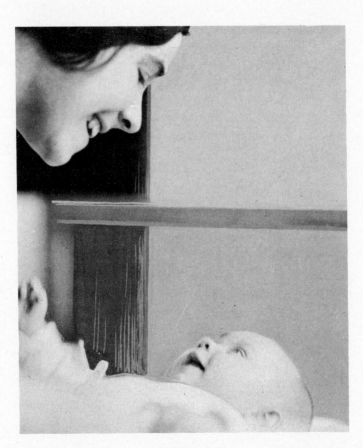

[ 32 ]

## Both Brothers Benefit

The senior brother who plays a friendly game with junior unconsciously learns a great deal about social relations. So does junior. Each learns from the other.

Social education depends on companionship in the home.

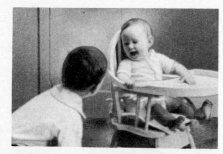

The baby: 32 weeks; the brother, 5 years

## Social Reciprocity in Mother and Child

## Children and Parents Socialize Each Other

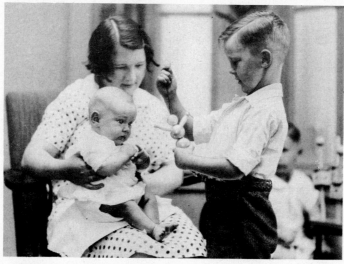

This 16-weeks-old baby watches his 7-year-old brother manipulate a toy, while another brother, 5, looks on in the background. Each benefits by the experience.

## Social Reciprocity in Father and Child

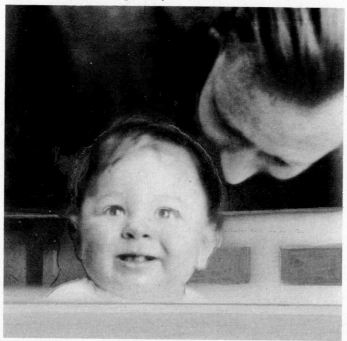

## Early Lessons in Humor

Fortunate the baby with good-natured companions. Laughter is a social safety valve. A sense of humor is a social gift, which keeps the spirit flexible.

Even in the nursery it is possible to cultivate this humanizing gift.

The hide and seek finger game, pictured below, has elements of humor for the baby, to say nothing of the father.

32-weeks-old baby; and 32-year-old father

# The Patterning of Personality Begins at Birth.

THE Baby is an individual from the moment of birth. He has inborn temperament and native constitution. They determine the way in which he will react to his environment.

He has deep-seated instincts of self preservation, like feeding, fearing, and fighting. But he also has a deep-seated interest in persons and in social experience. He is as hungry for social attention as he is for food. He needs both in proper amounts.

Wise affection makes him feel secure; independence makes him feel self-reliant. A balanced personality is neither too dependent on others, nor too self-assertive. In this sense the very first lessons in democratic living begin in the home.

### This Baby Has a Healthy Mixture of Independence and Sociability

Alone, he smiles on approach of brother . . .

Who gives him a leaf to play with . . .

He welcomes another brother . . .

And still another . . .

Four guests, but when they leave . . .

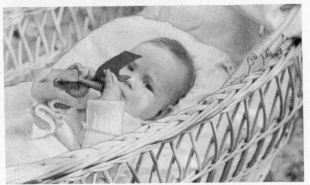

He finds his leaf sufficiently absorbing.

This boy is 24 weeks old. He regularly takes a nap by himself, and he is content to stay alone when he wakes up. But he smiles sociably on the approach of his benevolent brother, who gives him a leaf to play with.

Each elder brother is protective toward a younger. This is a social trait. But the baby brother remains reasonably self-sufficient when he is left alone to play by himself.

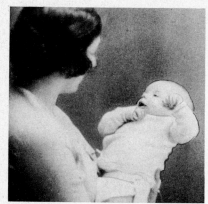 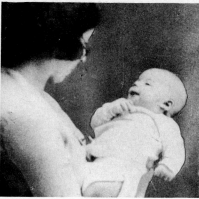 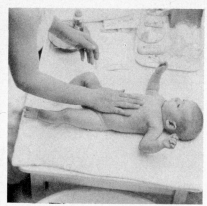 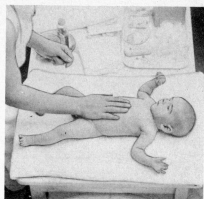

Amazingly early the human infant shows that he is a social being. At 8 weeks he looks intently at his mother's face.

He smiles in response to her voice and contacting hand. These are social responses, colored with emotion. Each day they multiply.

Every bath, every feeding, every service he receives helps to socialize the baby and gives him a sense of security and dependence.

But normal social development demands independence as well as dependence. Even a baby should not be made to feel too dependent.

## If He Responded Too Exclusively to His Mother He Might Easily Become Over Dependent
(This would injure his mental growth)

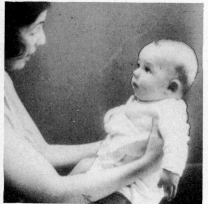 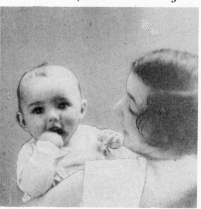 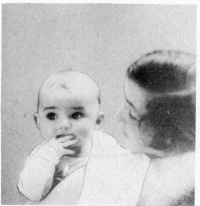 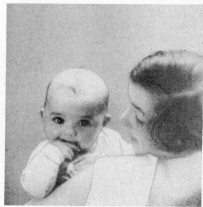

He reacts to her companionship . . .

But he also attends . . .

To other persons . . .

In his remoter environment.

## Within Wise Limits the Baby Must Be Allowed to Display Initiative, Self-Reliance, and Even a Little Refusal
(Like the 52-weeks-old boy below!) The infant must discover himself as well as others

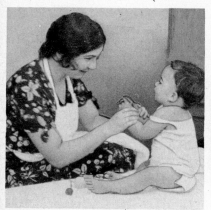 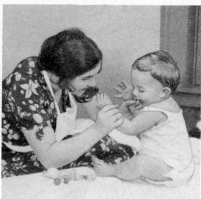 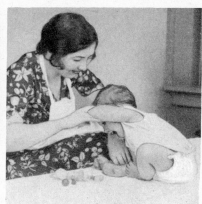 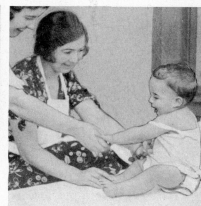

Invited to play . . .

He resists . . .

He refuses . . .

He compromises.

## At 32 Weeks: A Highly Sociable Baby Meets a Stranger

     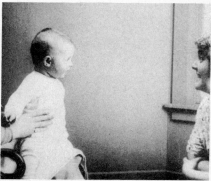

With eyes . . .

Arms . . .

Mouth . . .

Bouncing body . . .

And tongue . . .

He expresses friendliness.

# A MIRROR PLAYMATE: *A Baby does not know himself.*

THIS mirror playmate baffles the baby and leads him a chase. The mirror is an aid to self knowledge, both for infant and adolescent. But it may also deceive. Even at the age of one year the Baby does not recognize himself in his own image. He reaches out as he would to a playmate and tries to catch hold of the phantom.

Temperament as well as maturity determines how the Baby will react in front of the mirror. He may sober, he may smile, he may do both. He "talks"; he waves his arms; he brings hands and mouth to the glass. As he gets older he makes faces and plays a kind of peekaboo. His responses grow more social; but they are very naïve. It takes years of mental growth to acquire a full sense of self.

He sees a playmate.

Confidently . . .

he sets out . . .

to find him.

Perplexed, . . .

he approaches from the front . . .

then tries another route.

Mystified, he looks above . . .

returns . . .

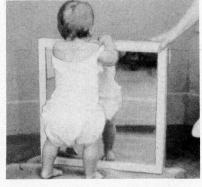

peers over . . .

and dashes behind.

Bewildered, he scurries back . . .

and keeps his eyes on him . . .

as he turns the corner.

Eluded, . . .

he quickly reverses his course . . .

to catch him . . .

off guard!

# CRYING: *the baby's first language.*

CRYING is language. Respect it. Try to understand its meaning each time it occurs. Babies do not cry without cause. They cry on account of pain, hunger, fear, anger, anxiety, bodily discomfort (chafing and wetness), sudden changes, strangeness, solitude, fatigue, and constriction of movements by tight clothes.

Screaming, crying, fretting, frowning, whimpering, sobbing are forms of emotional expression. They all need sympathetic interpretation. Generally the Baby's crying is justified. It is very unwise to go to extremes in letting the Baby "cry it out."

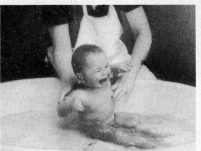

This 28-weeks-old boy enjoys the bath so thoroughly that he cries lustily when he is taken out . . .

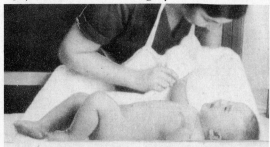

but his sensible mother takes the protest with wholesome calmness. She attempts no severe discipline. He will learn.

EXCELLENT MORALE at 36 Weeks: The clean up is none too pleasant. But this good-natured boy neither whines nor cries.

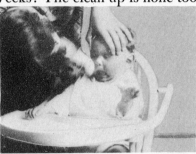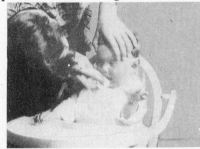

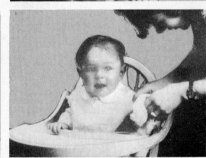

This Smile Expresses Timidity (24 weeks old)

This Smile Expresses Security (24 weeks old)

This 3-year-old boy was the baby whom you saw crying in his bath (above) when only 28 weeks old. Now he is comforting the crying of his baby sister.

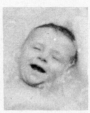

# SMILING: *Expresses emotion, mood and temperament.*

As the Baby grows he gains in powers of expression. Crying comes first, smiling next, and laughter later. Social situations and pleasant surprise delight even the young baby. At 6 weeks his face brightens, at 8 weeks he smiles, at 12 weeks he chuckles, at 16 weeks he laughs aloud.

Smiling and laughter vary with temperament. Some babies are expressive and demonstrative. Others are reserved, self possessed and sober. Respect these individual differences and do not stimulate laughing by excessive handling and tickling. The best smiles come naturally.

Every baby has a smile which is distinctive. As the baby grows his face moulds. As the expressive muscles of mouth, eyes, nose and cheek mature the smile takes on characteristic form.

## Social Smiles at 32 Weeks

## This Baby Demonstrates the Growth and Individuality of the Infant Smile

## Social Laughter at 32 Weeks

24 weeks          28 weeks          32 weeks

The baby looks particularly the stranger's smile.

40 weeks          68 weeks          72 weeks

He reciprocates with a smile and a laugh of his own.

## The Camera Tells the Story of This Baby's Smile—From 12 Weeks to 48 Weeks

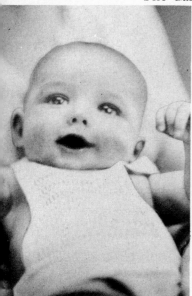
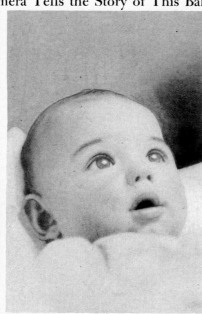
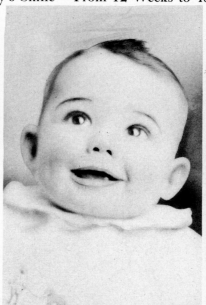
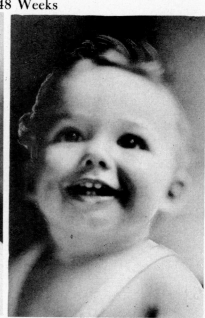

12 weeks: An early smile. Hands move up.

24 weeks: Quiet and sober. The facial muscles are relaxed.

32 weeks: The smile is now more complex. Eyes glisten, nose shortens, cheeks lift, bulge and dimple.

48 weeks: The smile is no longer toothless. The fold at the corners of the mouth is deeper and extends to nose.

# LANGUAGE BEHAVIOR:
## *The baby has varied forms of communication.*

HEALTHY social experiences are essential for normal language development. There are many kinds of language:—gestures, postural attitudes, facial expressions, crying, smiling, cooing, crowing, babbling, exclamations, names, phrases, sentences. Speech is the use of words as symbols of thought. It is the supreme human trait.

The foundations of speech are laid in infancy. Even in the first month the baby makes small throaty sounds. At 16 weeks he "talks" to himself. At about 32 weeks he utters syllables like *Da*. He can imitate only those sounds which he has already made in his babbling sound play.

By the end of the first year he may say one or two "words"; but at the beginning of the second year he usually goes through a period of jargon before he really begins to name objects and to articulate his desires. Children show great individual differences in the time when they begin to speak.

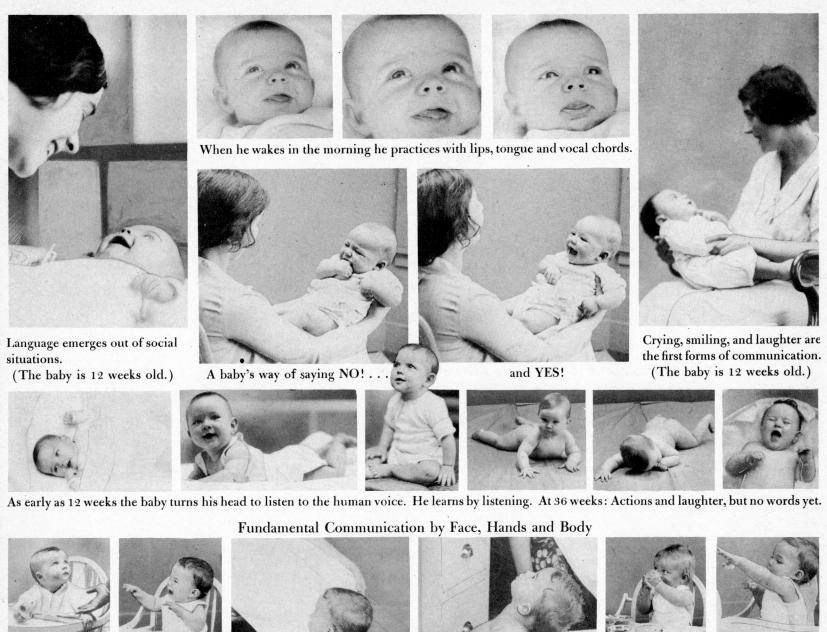

When he wakes in the morning he practices with lips, tongue and vocal chords.

Language emerges out of social situations.
(The baby is 12 weeks old.)

A baby's way of saying NO! . . .

and YES!

Crying, smiling, and laughter are the first forms of communication.
(The baby is 12 weeks old.)

As early as 12 weeks the baby turns his head to listen to the human voice. He learns by listening. At 36 weeks: Actions and laughter, but no words yet.

## Fundamental Communication by Face, Hands and Body

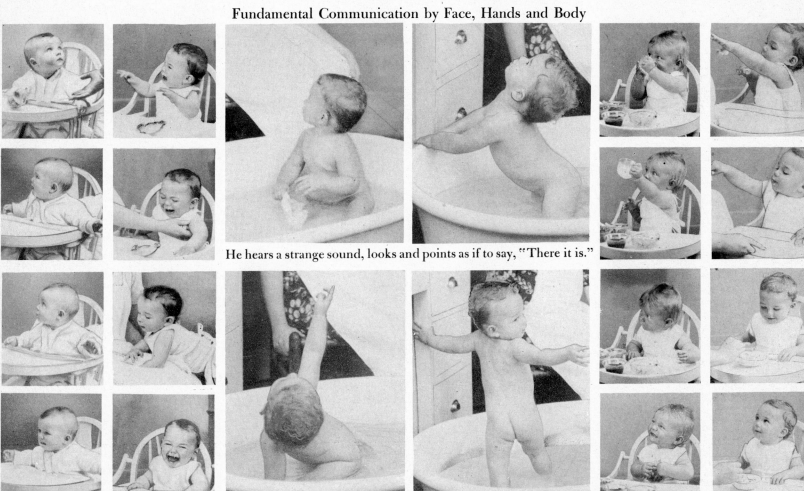

He hears a strange sound, looks and points as if to say, "There it is."

Timidity
(32 weeks)

Disappointment
(44 weeks)

The four pictures above show a silent conversation at 52 weeks. Gestures precede speech. A baby enacts sentences before he can speak them. He understands facial expressions before he understands the spoken words.

Sociability
(48 weeks)

Give and take
(52 weeks)

# A Baby's Day at Twelve Weeks of Age.

THE mental health of a baby depends on his everyday life. The foundation of mental hygiene lies in his daily behavior. The Baby's Behavior Day is the Baby's education. The doctor prescribes the Baby's diet and furnishes medical protection. But the home must furnish the psychological care. Wholesome care promotes mental welfare.

Every event in the Baby's Behavior Day has psychological value: his morning bath, his naps, his play, his self activity, his social behavior and above all, his feeding behavior. His personality is patterned through the cumulative experiences of his daily life. The home is his school!

## A Baby's Schedule Should Be Adjusted to His Age and Individuality. This Boy Wakes at Six

Asleep

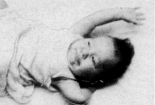

Waking

First feeding

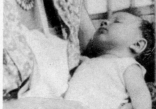

Asleep again

First nap

## The Bath Brings Experiences That Are Important Psychologically

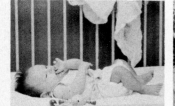

Crib play

Undressing

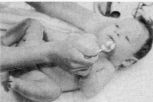

Cod liver oil

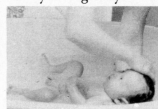

Shampoo

Natural exercise

## The Sun, Cod Liver Oil, and Fruit Juice Safeguard Against Infectious Disease

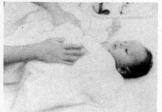

Drying

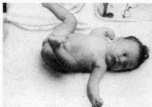

Sunning

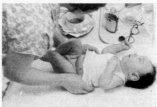

Dressing

Second feeding

Second nap

## Bountiful Sleep Is Essential. This Boy Sleeps 20 Hours Out of 24

Asleep again

Awake again

Third feeding

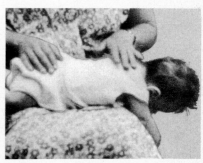

"Bubbling"

## Each Personal Contact and Service of His Mother Contributes to His Mental Growth

Third nap

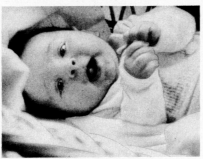

Vocal play on waking

Lap play

Floor play

## Play, Food, and Sleep Complete the Cycle of the Day

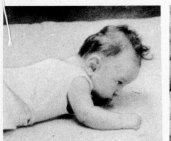

Natural exercise again

Fourth feeding

Evening sleep

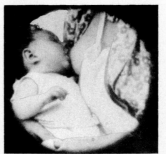

Fifth feeding

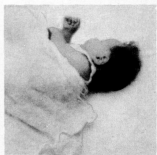

Night sleep

## A Baby's Day at Thirty-Six Weeks of Age.

THE activities and experiences of daily life constitute the Baby's education. As the infant grows older the cycle of daily behavior changes. At 12 weeks this boy slept 20 hours out of 24. Now he sleeps 18. He spends more time in the important business of play, exercising new powers of posture, locomotion, manipulation, language, and experimentation. A well regulated behavior day promotes his mental growth and mental health.

Every day in its succession adds a psychological increment. The pleasures, the trials, the routine, the adventure and the affection of each day become embodied in a growing personality.

Our 36 weeks old boy has put in a busy day. He accepts the close of day content. He makes no fuss when left alone, and in a few minutes he is sound asleep.

Even then the day is not done. For 12 continuous hours in the depths of sleep, the mysterious chemistry of growth builds its subtle networks and he wakes on the morrow a child more mature.

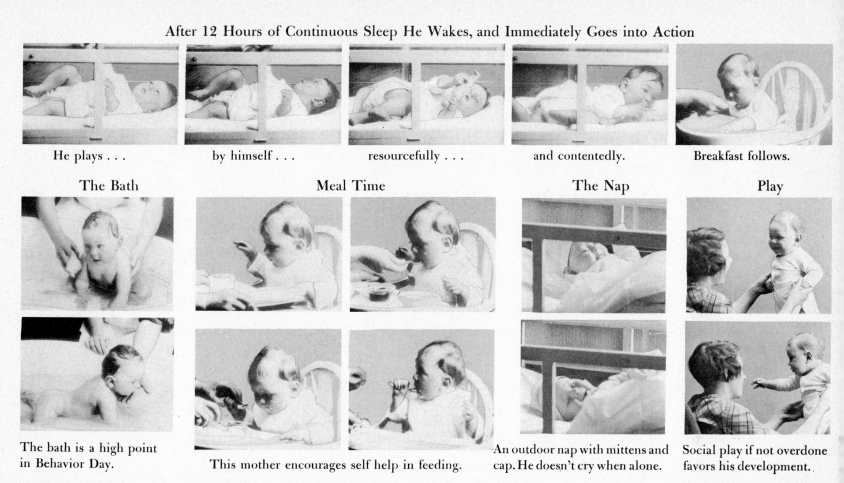

He plays . . .    by himself . . .    resourcefully . . .    and contentedly.    Breakfast follows.

**The Bath**    **Meal Time**    **The Nap**    **Play**

The bath is a high point in Behavior Day.

This mother encourages self help in feeding.

An outdoor nap with mittens and cap. He doesn't cry when alone.

Social play if not overdone favors his development.

### AFTERNOON FLOOR PLAY: A Striking Cinema Record of the *Very First* Successful Creeping in This Boy's Career

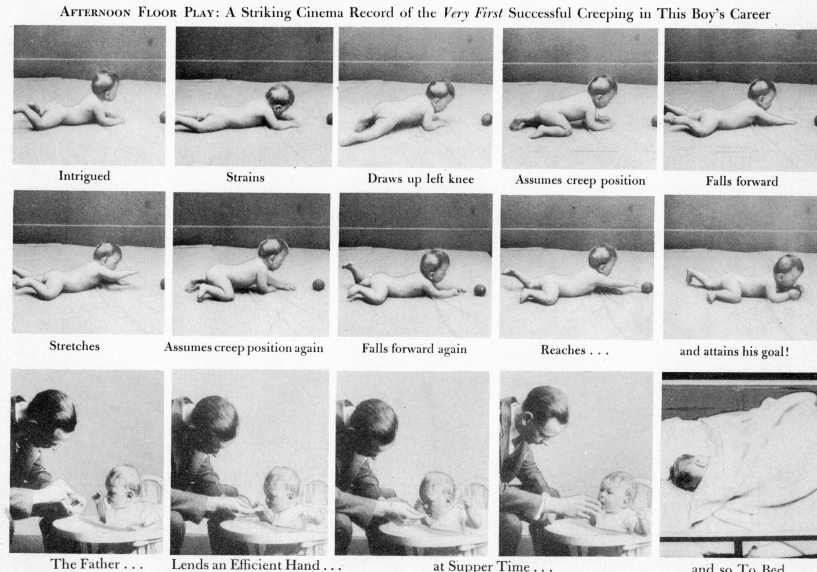

Intrigued    Strains    Draws up left knee    Assumes creep position    Falls forward

Stretches    Assumes creep position again    Falls forward again    Reaches . . .    and attains his goal!

The Father . . .    Lends an Efficient Hand . . .    at Supper Time . . .    and so To Bed

## *Behavior Patterns at One Year of Age.*

THE first year of life is a season of swift growth. It brings about amazing transformations of behavior pattern. Compare the newborn babe and the one-year-old. The newborn babe lies on his back limp and helpless, lacking control of eyes, hands, and feet. The one-year-old stands on his feet and uses his eyes and hands with almost adult precision.

He has become a complex individual capable of varied emotions, of flashes of insight and of persevering stretches of effort. He has talents and desires. He feels fear, anger, curiosity, affection, surprise, failure and success. He reflects his upbringing, but he also displays inborn, constitutional characteristics.

## The 40-Weeks-Old Baby Cannot Imitate a Scribble . . .

 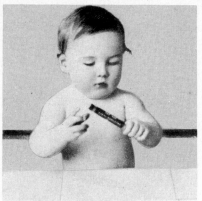

The 40-weeks infant watches the demonstration — but puts crayon to mouth instead of the paper.

## But the Year-Old Infant May . . . and Promptly

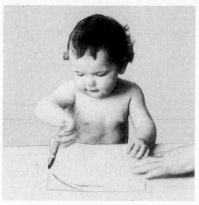 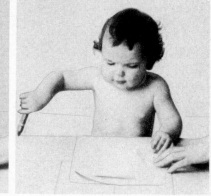

However, the year-old baby watches the demonstration — and promptly imitates it.

## The 40-Weeks-Old Infant Has No Concern for the Round Hole in the Board, and Does Not Bring the Block to the Hole

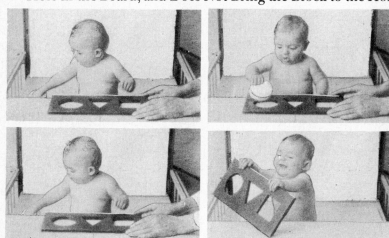

This baby looks through the holes, but makes no association between round block and round hole.

## The Year-Old Infant Has an Eye for the Round Hole in the Board; He Explores, Inspects and Inserts the Block

The year-old baby fingers, looks, makes an association, releases, places round block near round hole.

## The Year-Old Likes to Stand, and Ceaselessly Explores the World About Him

## THE BEGINNINGS OF SELF HELP AT ONE YEAR: He Can Hold His Cup (for a brief moment)

   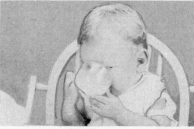

He cannot manage the cup altogether by himself, but he is on the road to greater independence.

# The Child's Maturity Determines What He Can Learn.

LEARNING and growth are inseparable. Teaching and training must wait on natural growth. What a child can learn depends on the ripeness of his nerve cells and nerve fibers. His capacities mature in a natural order: he pivots before he creeps; he sits before he stands; he builds a tower before he builds a bridge; he draws a circle before he can draw a square. Learning is limited by stage of maturity.

Nature cannot be hurried. It is useless to try to teach a child to draw a square when he is only beginning to draw a circle. Circles come first. He cannot imitate any action which is entirely new to him. All teaching should be tempered to his maturity. Don't go to extremes to teach bladder and bowel control before he is mature enough for such control.

## "Give-It-to-Mother" Is Too Hard a Problem for the 40-Weeks-Old Boy

## Imitation of Pat-a-Cake Is Too Hard at 36 Weeks; but Not at 48 Weeks

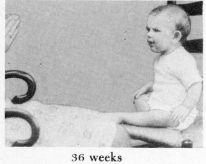 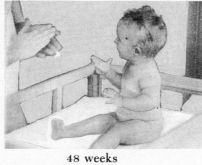 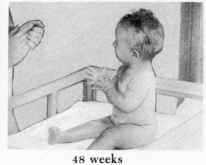 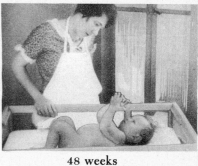

| 36 weeks | 48 weeks | 48 weeks | 48 weeks |

## This 36-Weeks-Old Baby Wants the Ball but Pivots Away from It. He Wants the Rattle and LEARNS to Pivot Toward It
(Pivoting is a natural ability which appears because of natural growth but which improves with experience)

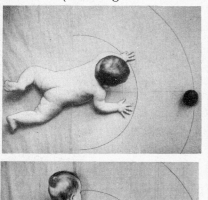 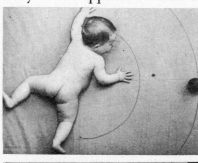 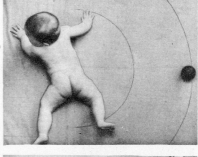 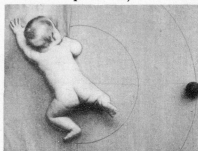

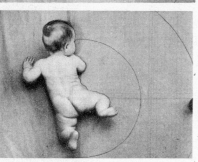 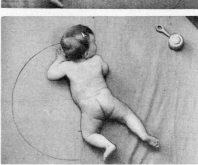 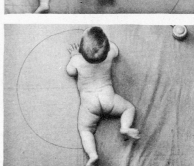 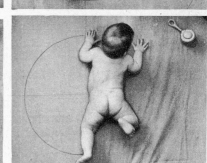

## A 40-Weeks-Old Baby Is Too Young to Imitate . . .    But at 52 Weeks This Baby CAN Imitate the Examiner

 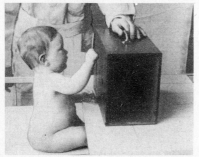 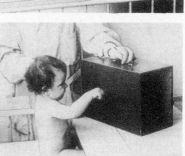 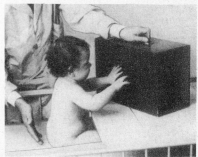

The examiner demonstrates how to insert a rod in a round hole of the box. The baby is attentive, but cannot imitate. He is 40 weeks old.

This baby is 52 weeks. She can imitate, but cannot insert the rod until the examiner puts the box at an angle.

# The First Three Months of Mental Growth.

WATCH the Baby grow! In the next few pages we bring the whole pageant of the baby's mental growth into orderly review. Ninety graded pictures are arranged in rows and columns to display the forward push of development which produces such interesting transformations in the patterns of behavior. Twelve age levels, from 4 weeks to 52 weeks, are depicted.

To study the characteristics of any one age read the columns up and down. To study the growth changes from one age to the next, read the row of pictures across the page. Compare as you follow through. In this way you can get a kind of motion picture impression of the whole sweep of development.

The sequence is dramatic. In the *first* three months the infant lies on his back; in the *second* three months, he sits propped up; in the *third,* he sits alone; in the *fourth,* he stands on his feet.

Development proceeds from head to foot. The eyes take the lead. At first he stares vacantly; later at windows and walls. Soon he looks at his mother's face or at her hand. He shifts his gaze from place to place. He discovers his own hand and looks at it a great deal. By the end of the first three months he actively inspects his surroundings. His eyes are under good control, but his head is still wobbly.

| 4 Weeks | 8 Weeks | 12 Weeks |
|---|---|---|

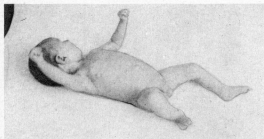

He lies with head turned to the side.

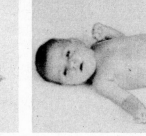

Legs are ever active. He can roll and swing his hips.

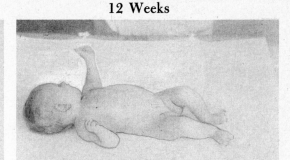

His head still favors the side position.

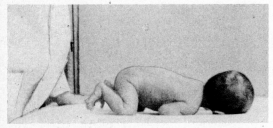

He rests on flexed knees, abdomen, chest and head.

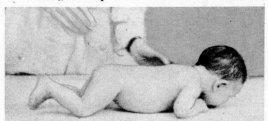

His legs are less flexed; his head is higher.

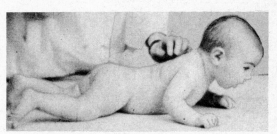

His head is reared. He rests only on legs, abdomen and chest.

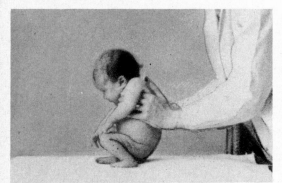

Head, trunk and arms sag when he is lifted.

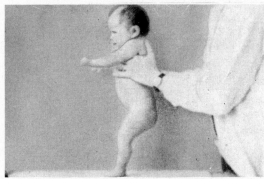

Head bobs. Legs extend. He supports a fraction of his weight.

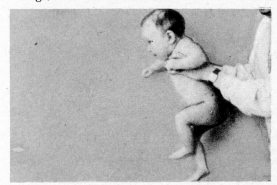

His head is more steady and erect, his trunk more rigid.

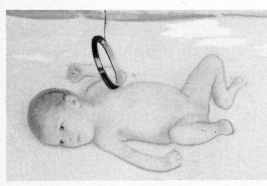

Keeps head turned to side. Disregards ring dangling above chest.

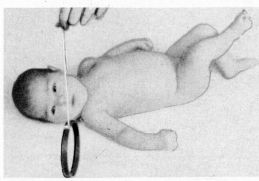

Looks at dangling ring both at side and above chest.

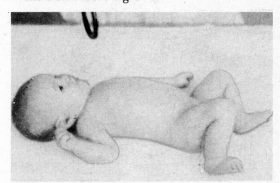

Looks at ring a long time and follows it from side to side.

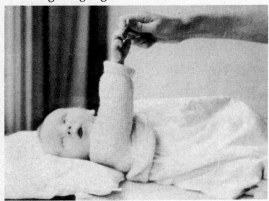

Does not heed social hand clasp. Keeps head turned to side.

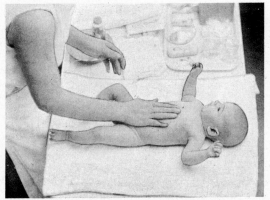

Responds to mother's contacting hand and to smiling.

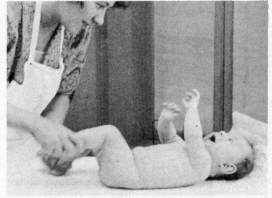

20 weeks: Recognizes mother. Face brightens when she talks to him.

## The Second Three Months of Mental Growth.

IN the first three months the Baby comes into command of the muscles which move his eyes. He inspects. Now in the second three months he comes into command of the muscles which support his head and move his arms. He reaches for things.

Eyes are no longer wobbly; and the head is ceasing to be so. It rests firmly on the shoulders. It rotates freely. Arms and elbows are becoming mobile; and in time the Baby reaches out for an object *on sight*. This means team work between eyes and hands. An important achievement. Note the second row of pictures. At 16 weeks he may not even contact the cube. At 20, he corrals it; at 24, he grasps it *as soon as he sees it*. Eyes and hands coordinate.

He holds his head erect before he holds his trunk erect. He gains control of his arms before he can manage his legs. Formerly his arms clung to his chest or remained at the side. Now he uses both of them to close in on an object. Not until later will he make his approach with one arm only. This is the growth season for arm control; therefore it is the time when he most uses and most enjoys a rattle.

|  16 Weeks | 20 Weeks | 24 Weeks |
|---|---|---|

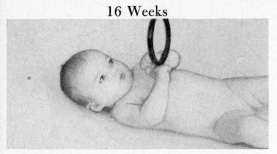

Head now favors a mid-position.

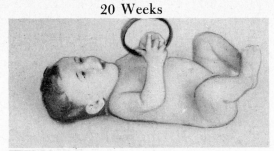

Hands close on a dangling ring.

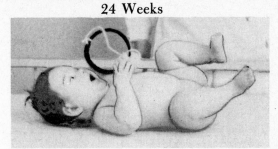

He grasps the ring and holds it with both hands.

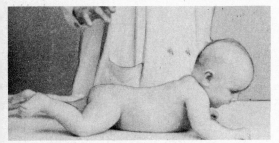

His legs are more extended. He rests more weight on forearms.

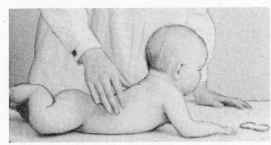

His arms are directed forward. He scratches the platform.

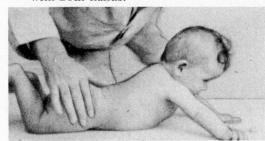

Now he rests on hands. At 8 weeks they were pressed under chest.

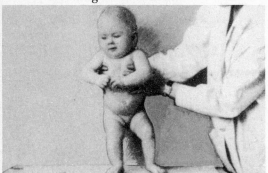

Head remains erect even while he is being lifted.

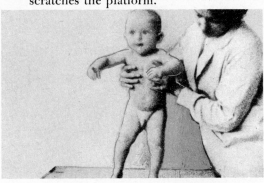

Now supports large part of weight; arms becoming more free.

Now or somewhat later he likes to bounce while held standing.

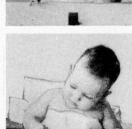 

Looks at cube but shifts gaze to own hand. Does not contact cube.

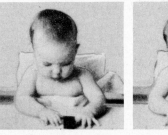

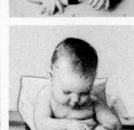

Brings hand in toward cube, contacts it but often fails to grasp it.

But now he grasps cube on sight, lifts and mouths it.

He laughs and responds to mother's conversation.

He turns head to sound of mother's voice.

He gives increasing social regard to mother and brother.

# The Third Three Months of Mental Growth.

THE Baby now comes into command of trunk and hands. He sits; he grasps and manipulates. In this quarter he reaches a halfway station on the road to upright posture. Trunk as well as head becomes steady. He sits alone. He can lean forward or sideward and then erect himself. He can hold his trunk rigid in a creep position even though he may not creep. But he is gaining mastery of his hands and can use them to push himself around in a pivoting circle on the floor.

His hands are now more flexible, more versatile. He usually reaches with one hand rather than two; he tilts his hand and uses his thumb in seizing objects. Holding an object in one hand he brings up the other hand and transfers the object from one hand to the other and then back again. He manipulates his toys in many different ways, banging, brushing, pushing, mouthing, inspecting. Thus he learns the properties of the physical world.

|  28 Weeks  |  32 Weeks  |  36 Weeks  |

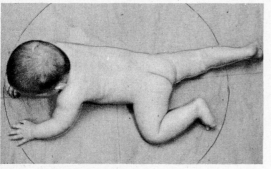 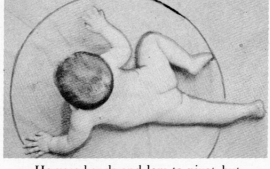 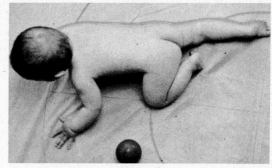

He rests his weight on hands, flexes legs but cannot swerve.

He uses hands and legs to pivot, but does not move forward.

He assumes a creeping position but still does not go forward.

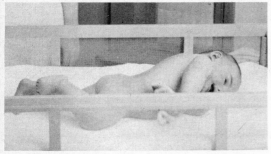 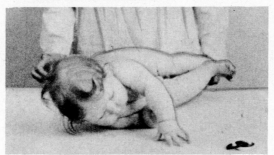 

Often he can roll from back to stomach.

He can roll (and pivot, too) to get an object.

Sometimes he can roll and pull himself into a free sitting position.

He sits almost alone, with body erect.

He sits alone and maintains brief balance even when reaching.

He can lean forward or sideward and then erect himself.

 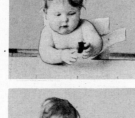   

He reaches even for a distant cube, bangs it on the table.

Inspects the cube in hand, also pays regard to third cube.

Now he brings one cube into definite combination with another.

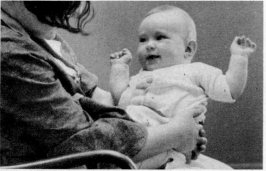  

Shows confidence in his mother. He observes facial expressions.

He is a bit distrustful of a stranger, however.

But now he gives his confidence to a visiting stranger.

## The Fourth Three Months of Mental Growth.

AND now the Baby comes into command of legs and feet,—and of forefinger and thumb. He stands; he pokes, plucks and pries. He is on the last lap of THE FIRST YEAR. Mouth, eyes, neck, shoulders, arms, trunk, hands, fingers, and feet,— this is the general order in which muscular control is built up. He sits before he stands; he goes on fours before twos; he cruises before he walks alone. He toddles before he runs. Indeed he cannot run in the first year. He must choose his own time to walk, because his ability depends on the ripeness of the nervous system and his body balance.

Upright posture and thumb opposition are almost unique human traits. Both are acquired in the last quarter of the year. Forefinger and thumb are now so specialized that the infant plucks a string by precise pincer prehension. He uses his forefinger to poke and pry into things. Thus he penetrates into the third dimension and the mysteries of hollow and solid, of container and contained. His social behavior, also, becomes more discriminating. He imitates but he remains an individual with a personality quite his own.

| 40 Weeks | 44 Weeks | 52 Weeks |
|---|---|---|

Now he can creep.

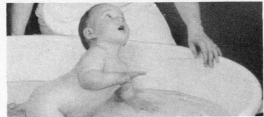

His trunk is more flexible; his balance improved.

He can stand, but he still creeps when he explores.

He can sit alone for some minutes and maintains good balance.

He can attain a standing position, at least with a little assistance.

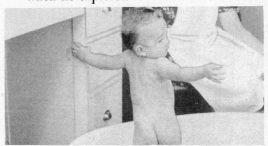

He can rise to standing and can lower himself.

He inspects clapper of bell, bangs bell on table.

Pokes clapper of bell exploringly.

Waves bell purposively and gleefully.

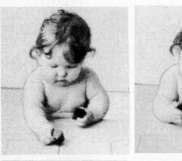  

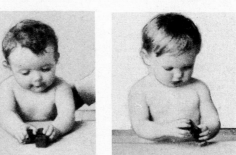 

Combines cubes. Seizes cube between forefinger and thumb.

Pushes and hits cubes about in experimental manipulation.

Brings one cube near and over another. *Almost* builds a tower.

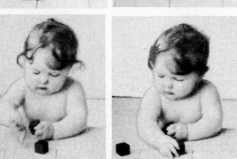 

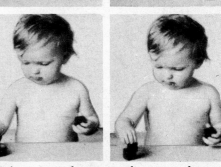

Not sufficiently social to respond to "Please give it to me."

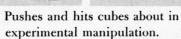

Now plays a responsive game of pat-a-cake.

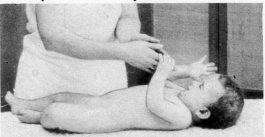

Beginning to "understand" words of command.

# *Early Drawing Reveals Laws of Growth.*

PAPER and crayon in the child's hands give us a visible record of certain behavior capacities. In the first three months he merely looks at a crayon; later on he grasps it, but crumples the paper. Toward the end of the year he begins to bring crayon upon paper. At 2 years he makes strokes. At 3 years he makes loops. At 4 years he can copy a cross. At 5 years he can usually draw a recognizable man. These progressive stages are not so much due to practice as to maturity. The development of drawing gives us some clue to the way in which the child himself develops.

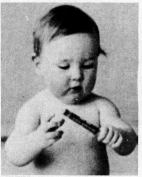     

| | | | | | |
|---|---|---|---|---|---|
| 40 weeks: Does not combine paper and crayon. | One year: Makes mark on paper. | Two years: Imitates vertical stroke. | Three years: Copies a circle. | Four years: Draws crude man. | Five years: Draws formed man. |

## One Year

Holds crayon at end.  Looks at paper.  Applies crayon to paper.  Draws crayon over paper.

## Fifty-Six Weeks

 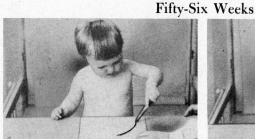  

Applies crayon.  Looks at his mark.  Looks at adult.  He makes another mark.

Three-year strokes . . .  and a smudge in water color . . .  But at four years, girl in a swing . . .  and a ladder.  At five years: A typical man for this age.

# Thus Did 21 Four-Year-Old Children Draw a Man!

In the fourth year children are passing from scribble and scrawl to representative art. Behold the evolution of man below. Fifty four-year-olds were asked to draw a man (no model or help). The samples from 1 to 21 illustrate a wide range of talent and maturity. The drawings were made without a model to copy.

Drawing No. 12 is a typical or average four-year-old man.

(But remember children develop at various rates.)

This was drawn by a superior four-year-old girl. Note duck, ducklings, earthworm and bench. In speaking of the bench the young artist said, "It started to be a cat, but there wasn't room enough. So it's a bench."

## Block Building Grows by Natural Stages.

Laws of growth control the progressive patterns of block behavior. Blocks are the universal toys of childhood. Block building, like drawing, is a form of play which elaborates with age. At 12 weeks the Baby merely looks at a block in front of him. At 20 weeks he corrals it. At 24 weeks he grasps it on sight. At 15 months and sometimes at one year he builds his first tower of 2 blocks; at 18 months, a tower of 3.

At 2 years he can build a higher tower and can lay his blocks in a row. At 3 years he builds a bridge of 3 blocks from a model. At 4 years a gateway of 5 blocks. At 5 years a stairway of 2 or more steps (from memory).

It takes a whole year and a half of brain growth to advance from a tower of 3 to a bridge of 3. Why should this be so? To think out an answer to this question, you will have to appreciate how a baby grows!

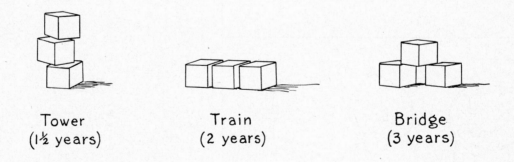

Tower
(1½ years)

Train
(2 years)

Bridge
(3 years)

### 12 Weeks of Progress

At 12 weeks: Looks at block and own hand.

At 20 weeks: Sweeps block in.

28-weeks-old baby grasps and holds two blocks and looks from one to the other.

At 24 weeks: Grasps block on sight.

40-weeks-old baby exploits each block in turn and brings them into combination.

### At 52 Weeks

The ONE-BY-ONE behavior pattern; ONE-BY-ONE from the table, ONE-BY-ONE back to the table. (Notice that the sequence begins and ends with three blocks.) This is the first growth stage in learning to count. Counting by handling comes before counting by words.

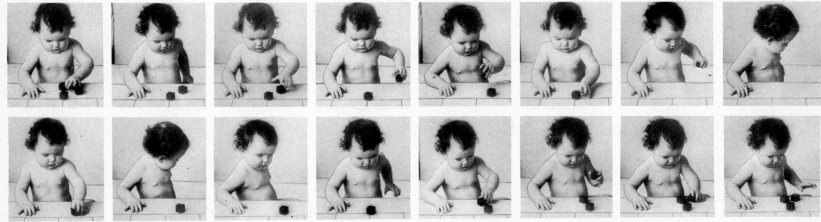

The First Triumphant Tower. And No One Taught This 52-Weeks-Old Baby How

### PROGRESSIVE PATTERNS OF BLOCK BEHAVIOR: Children from One and One-Half to Five Years of Age

One and one-half years: A small tower

Two years: A tall tower

Three years: He starts . . .

and proudly finishes a bridge.

Four years: A gateway

Five years: A ten-block staircase from memory

## The Preschool Years are Important Because They Come First.

THE *first five years of life* are fundamental for the simple but sufficient reason that they come first. Coming first in an indivisible sequence they inevitably influence all subsequent development. These fundamental five years determine mental health, in much the same way that the foundation and frame of a house determine the house. *In the first five years the child learns the alphabet of living.*

## At Home He Learns to Adjust to Parent, Brother, Sister and Playmates

A focus of social attention

A social advance

A friendly game

Playmates and pals

## In Nursery School and Kindergarten He Enters Further into Group Life

A pool for individual and co-operative play

A jungle gym for the large muscles

A tea party for social experience

## Through Play He Discovers and Educates Himself

He masters materials.  He masters a machine.

He molds ideas in sand.

He launches ventures in water.

He builds a grown-up world in imagination.

## He Builds Up Increasing Self-Reliance

Baby graduates from the lap . . .

to the sidewalk.

Takes journeys on his own.

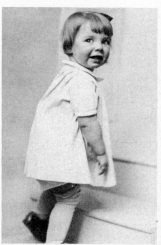

Goes on simple errands alone.

Makes his own repairs.

# The Baby Grows into a School Beginner.

THE school beginner is a baby of a larger growth. At 5 years of age the school beginner pictured on the opposite page displays personality characteristics which were already evident in infancy. Even as a baby he was energetic, agile, spirited, expressive, observant, alert. These are traits which the school should protect.

## Always He Has Been Alert and Inquisitive. He Takes Active Notice of All That Goes On Around Him

20 weeks

44 weeks

One year

One year

Five years

### He Is Always Sociable

Socially reactive in the cradle

A sociable host at the tea party

### The Same Intent Observer at 20 Weeks and at 5 Years!

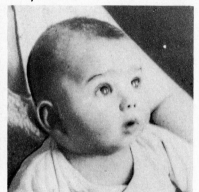

At 20 weeks — at 5 years

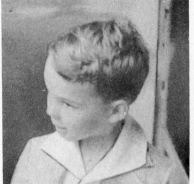

At 5 years — at 20 weeks

### Unchanged in 5 Years

He surveys his surroundings with characteristic curiosity.

He divides his attention between persons and things.

### He Draws and Constructs with Directness and Audacity

He makes a drawing . . .

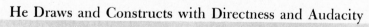

and here it is — a man, a fence, and a banner.

He also constructs a fence.

### He Is an Eager Explorer and Investigator — He Enjoys the New

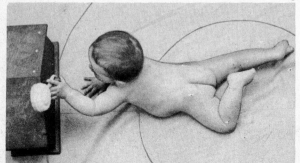

Mechanical bent and ability

Creative exploitation

Elementary construction

Advanced construction

## Another Baby Becomes a School Beginner.

EVERY child develops an individuality based on inherited traits. Some children, like some adults, are active and expressive; others are deliberate, quiet, self-contained. Parents and teachers should respect such individual differences in emotional makeup. Why should we expect all children to be equally gay, outgoing, and brisk?

The boy pictured on the opposite page is a sturdy, slightly reserved, moderately sociable and friendly child, whose characteristics were evident at one year as well as at five years of age.

He is also pictured in the series of action-photographs which make up the *end-papers* at the beginning and close of this book. These action photographs depict him at the ages of 40 weeks and 48 weeks, solving the ring-and-string problem. The figures in the lower right hand corner of the photographs show the elapsed time in seconds. Note particularly the gracefulness of his posture at the 17.7 seconds phase in the 48 weeks series.

## At 44 Weeks and at 5 Years He Deliberates Before He Acts

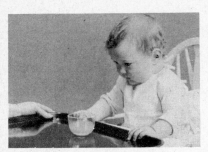
Can reach but first inspects.
(44 weeks)

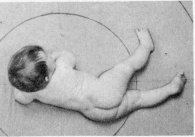
Can creep but prefers to watch.
(48 weeks)

Intrigued by the mechanical swing.
(5 years)

Studies the task in hand.
(5 years)

## During His First 5 Years He Has Been Quietly Sociable and Friendly in Temperament

36 weeks: Enjoys game with mother.

44 weeks: Notes stranger's approach . . .

Studies her with interest.

5 years: Chats with playmate.

## He Is Calm, but Not Indifferent, in New Situations (His problem here: A ring attached to a string)

Considers

Approaches

Contacts

Pulls in

Attains

Examines

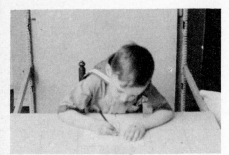
He executes with pleasure . . .

He is serious and earnest . . .

Enjoys his success.

At the age of 5 years he draws this man.

in work and play.

## Throughout the Pre-School Years He Shows Characteristic Emotions and Moods

Nine months

One year

Five years

Two years

Nine months

# Inborn Individuality Reveals Itself Early.

THE first task of parent and teacher is to understand the many signs by which a child expresses his nature and needs. Education at home and school is most effective when it takes account of inborn characteristics. Note how such characteristics show themselves in the girl pictured on the opposite page. At 5 years she proved to be definitely left-handed. The pictures strongly suggest that it was part of her nature even in infancy to prefer the left hand. This tendency was evidently inborn. Like all other inborn tendencies it should be respected. Harm may follow if deep-seated traits are injudiciously interfered with. Growth can be guided most successfully if the inborn characteristics and the maturity of the child are taken into account.

Every child has by birthright a distinctive maturing process which does much to shape his personality. The first fundamental task of parent and teacher is to *understand* the child.

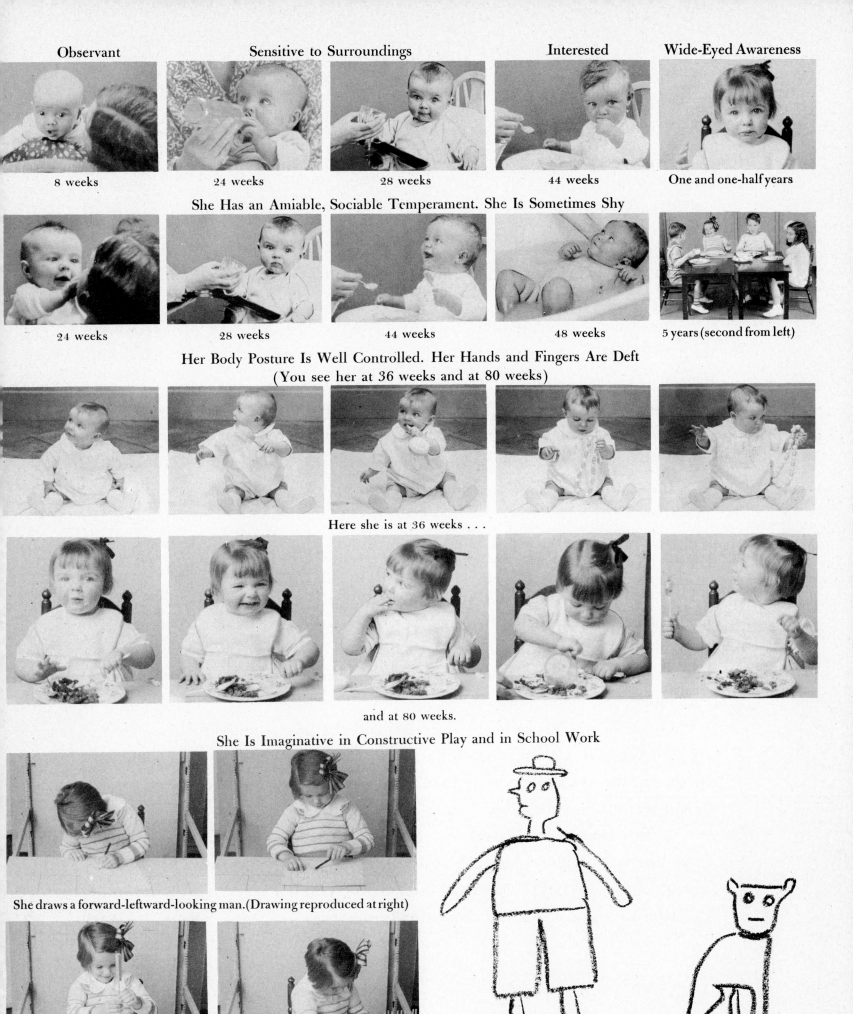

Observant — 8 weeks

Sensitive to Surroundings — 24 weeks — 28 weeks

Interested — 44 weeks

Wide-Eyed Awareness — One and one-half years

**She Has an Amiable, Sociable Temperament. She Is Sometimes Shy**

24 weeks — 28 weeks — 44 weeks — 48 weeks — 5 years (second from left)

**Her Body Posture Is Well Controlled. Her Hands and Fingers Are Deft**
(You see her at 36 weeks and at 80 weeks)

Here she is at 36 weeks . . .

and at 80 weeks.

**She Is Imaginative in Constructive Play and in School Work**

She draws a forward-leftward-looking man. (Drawing reproduced at right)

She builds a tall tower . . .            and then a fence.

She draws a man . . . and a dog.

# Infants are Individuals.

BABIES are persons. The portraits which adorn the next page will help to remind us that *Infants are individuals*. Each and every infant has a personality which is his own.

You have seen many infants in this book, but no two alike. Babies are not even born alike. They come into the world with different temperaments: each has his own personality assets and liabilities.

Our pictorial story has shown that babies pass through similar stages of development as they grow up. But each child grows up in his own particular way. Some children grow more rapidly than others. Some are early in speech; others in creeping or walking.

Look at the gallery of portraits and recall some of the babies whom you have seen in our pictorial series. Each is a distinctive individual. One baby is, by inborn nature, gay and sociable; another is sober, quiet, thoughtful. One baby is slender; another, stocky.

One is outgoing and self assertive; another is shy and retiring. When grown up, one will be talented in music; another, in mechanics, in art, or in manual skill. The strength of another will lie in character and in ability to manage persons. Every infant has certain valuable traits which should be found out early and which should be cultivated.

Our first problem is to try to understand the baby's individuality. Parents often try to make over a child into their own image. (Sometimes the father will have one image and the mother another!) Even before her baby arrives the mother may picture in imagination just the kind of child she would like to have.

If the newborn child does not fit to her pattern, she may feel disappointment. She may cling so strongly to her wish that she will actually try to transform the child. As though one child could be changed into another child! Every child has certain inborn characteristics which demand respect and tolerance.

[ 72 ]

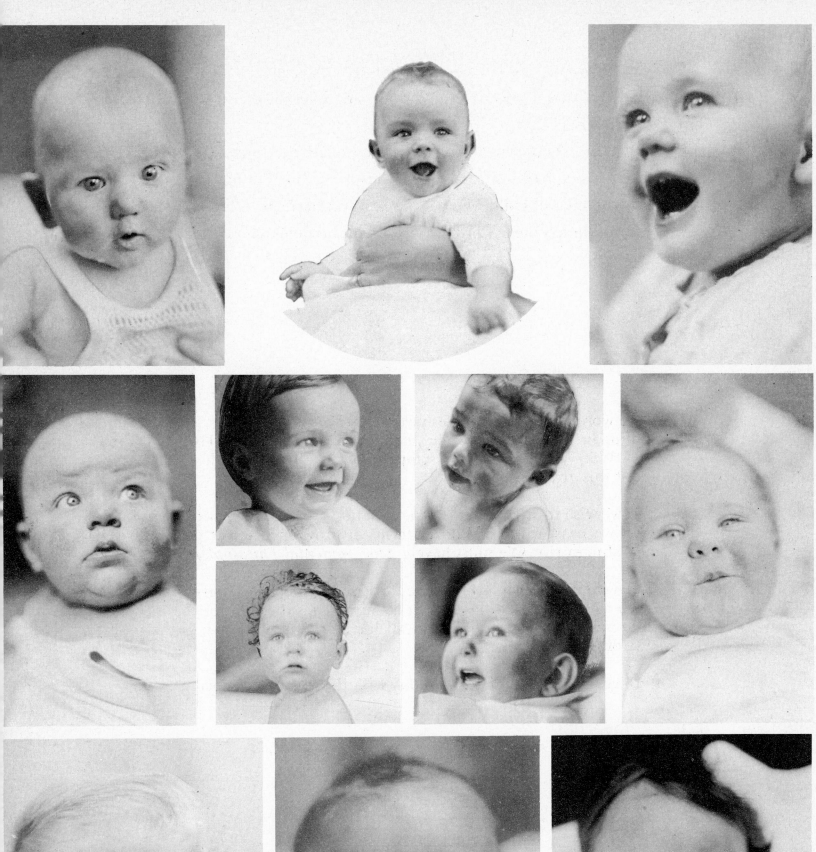
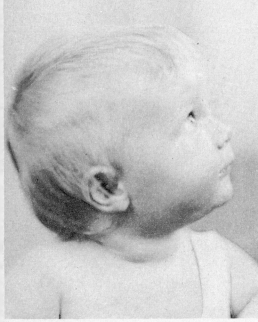
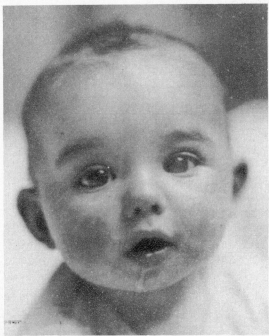
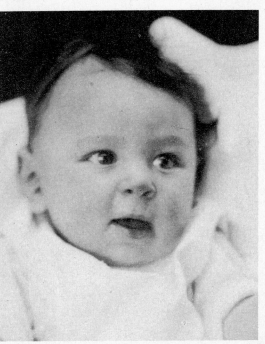

*Every child must do his own growing.* The best we can do is to guide and direct his growth. But that is a great deal. By assisting his growth we make him healthier in mind and happier.

A man may choose his wife. A girl may select the type of man she desires for a husband. This helps to insure favorable offspring. But the parents can not determine in advance the kind of child who will be born of marriage. That is the great adventure of life. It must be accepted. The newborn infant becomes an individual in his own right.

¶ In words and pictures we have given you a glimpse of the beginnings of human personality. We have told you something of HOW A BABY GROWS. Watch your baby sympathetically: he can teach you still more about this growth process.

¶ If we wish to do justice to his personality, if we are to respect his individuality, we must think of him in terms of growth, in terms of his developmental maturity. We must have *a developmental philosophy.*

¶ Developmentalism is the name for such a philosophy. Developmentalism is the very opposite of fascism. It acknowledges the right of the individual child and wisely recognizes that all his behavior is subject to the natural laws of development.

¶ Developmentalism is in harmony with the spirit of democracy.

# A Closing Word to Parents

## ENJOY YOUR CHILDREN

It is time for a closing word. In the pages of this book you have been given a glimpse of how human personality begins and how it grows.

In your own child you can witness that growth at first hand. It is a wonderful spectacle.

### The Pageant of Growth

Think of the transformations which take place in the first five years of life. The newborn baby is a bundle of helplessness. But how soon he gets command of his eyes and head! In four months he holds up his chin, he clutches with his active hands, he smiles a social smile. In a year he stands on two feet and presently begins to walk and to talk. At two years he speaks in phrases or even sentences. At three he feeds himself, builds a bridge of blocks (no small engineering feat), and converses in questions and answers. At four, he can go on errands by himself; and he works and plays in a cooperative group. At five, he is a self-contained and conforming little citizen. He likes to please, he is capable of sympathy, he takes pride in his clothes and kindergarten handiwork. He likes to be instructed. He responds to praise.

What an amazing advance beyond the helplessness of early infancy! All this progress has been accomplished because the baby is born with such remarkable powers of growth. When we consider what he accomplishes in those first five years, *we can have a deep faith in the constructive essence of growth. And with that faith we can enjoy our children.*

### The Guidance of Growth

If you think of your child in terms of his growth, you will see him in the best light. You will appreciate what he has already accomplished in the past; you will realize that with your guidance he is growing toward something better in the future. You will not

[ 75 ]

demand too much. You will have patience and understanding. After all, you cannot make him over. You can only guide him. He must do his own growing.

Does this mean that you will let him do just as he pleases? And that you will coddle him whenever he meets a difficulty? No. He must learn to do what is expected of him. But you must not expect too much. And you must be sure that he is mature enough to do what you expect, before you "discipline" him.

Let me illustrate with a simple but very true example. Do you remember the five babies pictured on page 15? All these babies were just the same age, about nine months old. This is the age when most babies begin to creep, but one of the babies could only crawl. He was unable to raise himself on his knees, even when his mother placed a ball before him. Now suppose that this mother had been very impatient. Suppose that she had said to herself, "He *ought* to creep; he is lazy and he is stubborn." Suppose that in her impatience she "disciplined" the baby by spanking him! What a sad mistake that would have been! Of course, she didn't spank him. She didn't expect too much. She knew that it was perfectly natural for a baby to go through a crawling stage before he reaches the creeping stage. She also knew that some day he would creep and that in due time he would also walk on two feet. She was not surprised when even at the age of fifteen months the baby sometimes preferred creeping to walking. And never once did she punish the baby because he lacked control of his muscles.

When he began to walk she encouraged him; but she never forced him. When his balance was poor she held him by *two hands*. Later he needed only *one hand* for support. Still later she left him to toddle all *alone*. She helped him just enough. And she did not expect too much. She used guidance rather than punishment. It was easy to be patient. because she knew that someday her child would walk. As a result she enjoyed watching the whole process by which he gained control of his muscles. She enjoyed her child.

### Guidance Based on Understanding

But as he grew older, he became more troublesome. He pulled at the curtains, he overturned the wastebasket, he broke his toys, he spilled his milk, he ran away when you called him, he threw things on the floor, he soiled himself, he didn't mind. Often he seemed to do the very opposite of what he was asked to do. He surely tried his mother's patience.

[ 76 ]

When her patience gave out she was tempted to spank him soundly. Perhaps she shook him, or shouted at him, and threatened him. Instead of enjoying her child, she was irritated by him! And this may have been the very mother who was so wise and patient when her child was learning by slow stages to crawl, to creep, to stand, to walk. With the best of intentions, she now feels that she must "discipline" her child. She thinks she must be stern and severe. She becomes so emotional about the child's disobedience that she no longer takes pains to understand his behavior. She forgets all about the process of growth. She forgets that *the best "discipline" is guidance based on understanding*.

Fathers likewise forget that physical punishment is a very poor substitute for intelligent guidance. Children should be managed rather than chastised. It is better to do nothing at all than to be too severe with a young child. We do not whip a child because he falls down when he is learning to walk. Should he be whipped when he "falls down" in his conduct? He may be altogether too immature to really appreciate what you expect of him.

For example, the 2½ year old child gets altogether too many spankings. He has a reputation of being contrary and obstinate. Parents forget that he is still almost a baby; that he cannot always make a clear distinction between *right* and *wrong*, between *yes* and *no,* and *come* and *go.* He is just at that stage of growth where everything immediately suggests its opposite. Every street is a two-way street for him and he has very weak powers of making a choice between two alternatives. So he often does the very opposite of what you ask; and thereby gets a reputation for contrariness. But you can manage him if you are not too determined and too stubbornly (?) strict! He is not as perverse as he seems. In a few short months he will show much greater capacity for obedience. He *grows* into this capacity with your guidance. When he is 3 years old he has himself better in hand. Far from being contrary, he tries to please, because he now knows how to make simple choices. He has a higher degree of self control; but even the 3-year-old child will "fall down" in his conduct if you expect too much, and if you get too severe with him.

One does not have to be so grimly determined! Of all things in Nature nothing is more marvellous than the cycle of child development. No spectacle offers a more intriguing mixture of the predictable and the unpredictable. Why not enjoy it?

[ 77 ]

There is another reason why we should avoid all forms of harsh or fascist discipline. We live in a democracy. And the democratic way of life begins at home. We can respect the dignity of the individual even in his tender years.

And so in all problems of child management, at every age, we must learn to think in terms of the child's maturity. — It takes time to grow. — The Scriptures say, "the earth bringeth forth fruit of herself: first the blade, then the ear, after that the full corn in the ear." — As with a plant, so with a child. His muscle control, his mind, his morals, his spirit, grow by natural stages and sequences. — To guide him aright, to enjoy him aright, we need to know How a Baby Grows!

Arnold Gesell

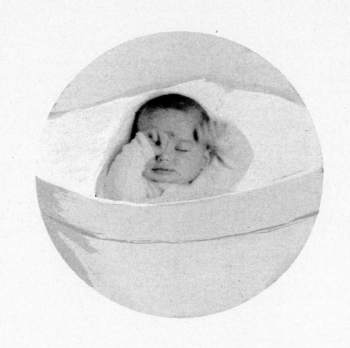

*How were all these photographs taken?* For a detailed answer the reader must be referred to the introductory chapters in volumes one and two of An Atlas of Infant Behavior, published in 1934, by The Yale University Press. The atlas is illustrated with 3,200 action photographs, based on cinema records made over a period of seven years, in connection with a research program supported in part by The Rockefeller Foundation.

The pictures in the present volume were derived from these cinema records and associated stills. Both present and former members of the staff of The Clinic of Child Development of the School of Medicine, Yale University, participated in the underlying systematic investigations, which are reported elsewhere. We are indebted to the cooperation of The Yale University Press and of the Des Moines Register-Tribune. Mr. and Mrs. A. W. Rushmore rendered invaluable assistance in typographic and technical details. I am also greatly in debt to Mrs. Louise B. Ames, Curator of The Yale Films of Child Development.

A. G.

8.4

10.8

40.9

43.7

11.7

13.6

23.3

26.5